Bush Flying

TAB
PRACTICAL
FLYING SERIES

Bush Flying

Steven Levi
Jim O'Meara

Graphics by Karen Gillespie
Photography by Brian Nelson

TAB Books
Division of McGraw-Hill

New York San Francisco Washington, D.C. Auckland Bogotá
Caracas Lisbon London Madrid Mexico City Milan
Montreal New Delhi San Juan Singapore
Sydney Tokyo Toronto

pbk 4 5 6 7 8 9 10 11 12 13 DOC/DOC 9 9 8 7 6 5

Library of Congress Cataloging-in-Publication Data

Steven, Levi C.
  Bush flying / by Steven Levi and Jim O'Meara.
    p. cm.
  Includes bibliographical references and index.
  ISBN 0-8306-6462-9   ISBN 0-8306-3462-2 (pbk.)
  1. Bush flying. I. O'Meara, Jim. II. Title.
TL711.B88S74 1990
629.132'5216—dc20   90-21066
                                              CIP

Acquisitions Editor: Jeff Worsinger
Book Editor: Tracey L. May
Director of Production: Katherine G. Brown
Book Design: Jaclyn J. Boone
Series Design: Jaclyn J. Boone   PFS
Cover photo courtesy: Doug Geeting Aviation, Talkeetna, Ak.   3462

To the bush pilots of Alaska

Contents

Introduction

THE PRIMARY REASON FOR THE WRITING OF *BUSH FLYING* WAS A noticeable lack of readable books on bush flying. While we found there were plenty of books on the intricacies of navigation and mountain flying, for instance, we could not find a general book on bush flying. *Bush Flying* fills this gap.

This book is aimed at the pilot who is interested in learning about the skills that bush pilots in Alaska must master. Not all the pilots who will read this book live in areas where they will have to master mountain flying skills, but *Bush Flying* has a little something for everyone, from handling live cargo to navigation, from reading the weather like a book to surviving a plane crash. It is designed to give the reader, whether a seasoned pilot or a novice, a few tips per chapter that he or she can take to heart.

We have made a special effort to make sure that this book is readable. Far too often the best information in an aviation book is so buried in complex, incomprehensible paragraphs that it takes a rocket scientist on No-Doz to decipher it. We were determined to avoid this shortcoming. *Bush Flying* was written to entertain and educate the reader at the same time—without his having to spend hours in a dictionary.

This book would not have been possible without the help and assistance of many people and institutions, including the Reeve Museum, the Anchorage Museum of History and Art, David Powers, Rachel Nelson, Chapman College, Doug Geeting, Jeff Pull, *Alaska Flying Magazine*, Kevin Ferris, Andy Fowler, the late Tom Parker, and Ben Gillespie.

1
The Old and the Bold

FROM THE GRAVEL STRIP RUNWAYS OF THE MOST REMOTE COMMUNITIES IN Alaska to the pavement of Merrill Field in Anchorage and Weeks Field in Fairbanks, there is an old saying that bush pilots understand well. "There are old pilots," the saying goes, "and there are bold pilots. But there are no old, bold pilots."

There is something dramatic about the Alaskan bush pilot that has captured the attention of the world. He is a giant in the world of aviation, the stuff of which legends are made. These are the men, and a few women, who flew by the seat of their pants, in open cockpits when the temperature was well below zero, over the roughest terrain in North America, in some of the worst weather on the planet. Season after season, year after year, these pilots loaded their planes, climbed into the cockpit, and headed out over the Alaskan bush, that part of the Last Frontier that even today is not connected by road to the Lower 48. Whether it was groceries to remote villages, furs to a rendezvous in Anchorage, or the injured to a hospital in Juneau, these pilots were, quite literally, the lifeline of Alaska.

It is hard to explain to someone living in the Lower 48 just how important the airplane has been to Alaska. While the rest of the United States has long since shifted from air carriers to trucks for the bulk of its deliveries, in Alaska more than one-third of the population lives in the bush. There are no roads connecting these communities, and the Alaskans who live here still depend exclusively on the airplane.

Even today in Anchorage, Alaska's largest city, meat and vegetables are labeled "air fresh," meaning that they were flown in within the last two days. Well into the 1960s, Anchorage was still so dependent on the airplane that breakfast lovers subsisted on "cold storage eggs," eggs that had been almost frozen in Seattle before making their journey to the grocery stores of the northland. Even as late as 1969, Alaskan television was on what was known as a tape delay. Humorously, it was noted, that was because the video tape was always delayed.

CBS News in Seattle, as an example, would record its broadcast day and then send the tape north by plane. The 6 P.M. CBS news was recorded live at 3 P.M. in Seattle and then placed on a 4 P.M. flight for Anchorage. The three-hour flight, plus the one-hour difference in time zones, allowed the 6 P.M. New York feed to be broadcast at 7 P.M. the same day in Anchorage. But this system only worked if the weather was good and the planes operational. That wasn't something anyone wanted to bet on.

News was sent and broadcast as soon as possible, of course, but other programs were a week behind the national schedule. At least that was the way it was supposed to be. Many Alaskans tell stories of watching Christmas specials in April or professional football playoffs in February.

Further, because of the routing of the tapes to several cities, those Alaskans who traveled frequently within the state often saw the same program three or four times because they and the tape were flying on the same planes. A business person traveling in Southeast Alaska could see the same movie in Juneau, Sitka, Petersburg, and Ketchikan. Whenever this happened, Alaskans were famous for saying, and ". . . the movie always ended the same way."

Prior to the introduction of the airplane, the transportation of goods into the Territory of Alaska was strictly by barge and steamship. Goods destined for Southeast Alaska were transferred to smaller ships, which in turn supplied the scattered communities of the Alexander Archipelago—known today as the "Panhandle" or simply "Southeast." Supplies ordered by Anchorage and Fairbanks were offloaded in Seward and placed on the Alaska Railroad. For the bush communities of the interior, the barges and steamboats went to Nome, Kotzebue, or St. Marys. From there, the cargo went up river to cargo transportation hubs. Smaller boats took it up the tributaries of the Yukon and Kuskokwim to docking areas where it was moved to its final destination by horseback, wagon, or on someone's back. Travel was slow because the going was arduous. Goods were expensive because the cost of transportation was so high.

Then, with the introduction of the airplane, goods began to move faster and became cheaper as well. Better yet, miners and trappers were assured a consistent, year-round supply of goods. Remote communities were assured of somewhat fresh vegetables as opposed to no vegetables at all. Mail, which had previously taken weeks by dogsled to reach the largest of the bush communities, could now be transported from Fairbanks in a matter of a few hours if the weather was good.

The era of aviation in Alaska opened in 1923. A school teacher, Carl Ben Eielson, who had flown with the United States Army Air Corps during the First World War, was able to convince postal authorities in Washington D.C., to authorize a contract for mail delivery by air between Fairbanks and McGrath, a small bush community about 250 miles away. When the contract for the mail was approved, the Postal

Service shipped Eielson a DeHavilland DH4. Because there was no building large enough to house the plane, Eielson and some friends assembled the aircraft at the end of what logically would be Alaska's first landing strip: a Fairbanks baseball diamond.

On February 12, 1924, Eielson was set to make history. He started the engine, bounced the plane down the length of the baseball diamond, and lifted the DH4 off the ground. Once airborne, he headed west for McGrath. The air was clear and the temperature five below zero on the ground—and substantially colder for Eielson who was flying in an open cockpit.

The flight was uneventful except for one brief, ironic moment. Eielson spotted Fred Milligan on the trail below and waved to him. Milligan had the winter dogsled mail contract over the same route. Eielson was going to cover in three hours what Milligan usually ran in 20 days.

Milligan was caught by surprise and later commented excitedly to his friends, "The pilot leaned out and waved at me with his long, black bearskin mittens. He couldn't have been much higher than the tree tops." When the dog sledder saw the plane, he knew his mail contract days were numbered. He could see the writing in the sky. "I decided then and there," he later noted, "that Alaska was no country for dogs." Milligan switched from dogs to airplanes and, at the end of the Second World War, was an Airport Traffic Manager for Pan Am.

As for Eielson, at 11:45 A.M., he landed on the frozen Kuskokwim River and bounced to a stop, the first plane to ever land at McGrath. He dropped off his load of letters and collected 60 pounds of mail waiting for him in McGrath. Unfortunately, he had turned his engine off during the unloading and loading. It took three hours to restart the machine. As a result, the first mail delivery to Fairbanks was three hours late.

The history of bush flying in Alaska is a mixed bag, so to speak. There were hundreds of men and women who made their living transporting cargo, mail, passengers, and occasionally animals (some living; some dead) into and out of the remote communities of Alaska. They worked year round, sometimes in weather that would close a modern airport.

Recommending a good book on Alaskan bush pilots is like looking over a meat counter and asking the butcher "What's good?" There is a tale for every taste. The classics in the field are Jean Potter's *Flying North* (Curtis Publishing, 1945) and *Flying Frontiersmen* (Macmillan, 1956). Beth Day's saga of Bob Reeve, *Glacier Pilot* (Holt, Reinhart Winston, 1957), was so popular in Alaska that the semi-pro ball team in Anchorage was named the "Glacier Pilots." Of more recent vintage are *The Last of the Bush Pilots* by Harmon Helmericks, (Knopf, 1970), *Mudhole Smith* by Lone E. Janson, (Alaska Northwest Publishing Company, 1981), *Wager with the Wind, the Don Sheldon Story* by James Greiner, (Rand McNally, 1974) and Jack Wilson's *Glacier Wings and Tales* (Great Northwest Publishing and Distributing Company, 1988).

Time-Life Books produced a very inferior book on bush pilots, titled *The Bush Pilots*, which is only worth recommending for its photos of Alaskan bush pilots. There are excellent photos of Art Woodley as well as an entire section on the deaths of Carl Ben Eielson and Earl Borland. One of the more unusual photos is of Bob Reeve with mountain climber Bradford Washburn. Both men are up to their ankles in mud and standing as though everybody did this kind of thing. Washburn's ascent of Mt. Lucania, incidentally, was featured in *Life* magazine, September 27, 1937. At that time, Mt. Lucania was the tallest unclimbed peak in North America.

BOB REEVE

Rather than try to offer the vast array of Alaska's flying pioneers, three characters of note sum up the tenacity and verve of Alaska's aviation heritage. One of the best known today is Bob Reeve, the legendary glacier pilot, who founded Reeve Aleutian Airways (FIG. 1-1). Reeve Aleutian is still in business today, a regional carrier and the 27th largest air cargo operation in the United States. It employs over 250 employees who are scattered along 1,500 miles of the Aleutians, roughly the same distance as from Washington D.C., to Cheyenne, Wyoming.

Reeve was born in Waunakee, Wisconsin, but showed an early aptitude for wandering. At 15 he enlisted in the United States Army, after swearing he was 18, and worked his way up to infantry sergeant before the end of the war. After the war he

Fig. 1-1. *Bob Reeve in winter dress.*

Reeve Museum

4

worked as a handyman and "swamper" for a barnstormer. (A "swamper" was someone who traded his services for flying lessons.) "Eating was awfully irregular," Reeve later noted. "We missed many meals to buy parts for the plane."

In 1929 Reeve headed to South America where he piloted the Pan American-Grace Airways mail run. Two years later he was back in the United States, a rich man. But the wealth was not to last. "I'd earned money like a horse. But I spent it like a jackass." By 1932 he was flat broke—again—and decided to head north. Stowing away in the chain locker of a steamer, he arrived in Valdez, Territory of Alaska, with two dollars in his pocket and hope in his heart.

Looking for a job in Valdez, he discovered a wrecked Eaglerock plane, which he repaired and then rented. Some neighbors helped him clear a cow pasture for a landing strip and he was in business again! His first trip, however, was almost his last. Two prospectors convinced him to fly to Middleton Island in Prince William Sound with the solid assurance that there was a "big, long beach" where he could land. When they arrived, there was no beach to be found.

Reeve decided to land on what he thought was a sand bar. The sand bar turned out to be "fluffy, pea soup sand," which shifted when his wheels hit. When the craft came to a stop, it was 1,000 feet from shore with a broken propeller in a rising tide. Using a block and tackle he found on shore, Reeve hauled the Eaglerock ashore before the waters could swamp it. Then the three men had to drag the plane a mile before they found a place suitable for Reeve to take off. (So much for that "big, long beach.") Reeve straightened the prop blades with a wrench and took off.

But it was not to be his day. Valdez was socked in so he headed to Seward, an hour away. He landed with less than five minutes of gas in his tank (FIG. 1-2).

In 1933 Reeve found his niche in what became known as "glacier flying." It was a risky enterprise; so risky, in fact, that even the legendary Harold Gillam refused to try. Glacier flying involved flying men and materials onto glaciers. Even today this is a risky business. The surface of a glacier is rutted and deep crevices are hidden by snow cover. Worse, it is very difficult for the pilot to judge where the sky ends and the snow begins. Once, for example, Reeve misjudged the snow, hit some boulders covered by snow, and his plane bounced 200 feet into the air. When asked what landing on a glacier was like, Reeve once responded that visibility was "like sticking your head in an enamel pail."

The tightest moment in Reeve's life came when he dropped Brad Washburn off on Walsh Glacier. Once on the ice floe the weather turned miserable and snow began to fall. When Reeve tried to take off the first time, the plane wallowed in the snow. Then came rain. The storm lasted for four days. By then it was apparent to everyone that Reeve would probably be forced to leave the plane on the glacier and come back the next winter when the snow could be packed hard for a runway (FIG. 1-3).

"You can leave the plane here and walk out," suggested Washburn.

"I'm no mountain climber," snapped Reeve, "I'm a pilot. You can skin your skunk—I'll skin mine." Then he stripped his plane of every ounce he didn't absolutely, positively need. He flattened the propeller and clambered aboard. The Fairchild ran

Fig. 1-2. *Bob Reeve up to his ankles in mud.*

Fig. 1-3. *Bob Reeve taking off from the appropriately named Valdez Mudflats.*

about 10,000 feet trying to get enough airspeed to take off when Reeve ran out of runway. When he came to the edge of the glacier, facing a 500-foot drop, he went right over the top. "The dropoff gave the ship just enough forward speed. That was the greatest feeling in my life bar none," Reeve later recalled.

Washburn, who had been flown into remote mountain valleys all over the world, watched from the safety of the glacier and noted, "Bob Reeve is without question the finest ski pilot and rough country flyer I have seen anywhere."

Reeve operated as a glacier pilot, supplying trappers and miners in the remote regions of Alaska until the outbreak of the Second World War. Then he operated as a cargo carrier for the United States Army. The Japanese had taken the last two islands of the Aleutians—Attu and Kiska—and the Army was trying to dislodge them. It was a lengthy process and ended with the second bloodiest battle of the Pacific Theater. American forces stormed Attu on May 11, 1943. After 18 days of heavy fighting, the Japanese made a suicide charge, after which only 28 Japanese remained alive on the island. Japanese losses were estimated at 2,700.

Flying the Aleutians was as dangerous as glacier flying. Operating in the most hostile weather the world had to offer, Reeve kept the United States military supplied throughout the war. After the war, he continued to supply the military bases and communities that dot the 2,000-mile chain of islands. What makes Reeve Aleutian Airways so unusual even today is that their planes fly in what the aviation experts declare to be the worst flying weather in the world. In many spots on the chain it was—and is still—possible to have two 50-mile-an-hour winds blowing in opposite directions at different ends of a runway. The Aleutians are also the only place in the world where you can have fog and 50-mile-an-hour winds at the same time.

HAROLD GILLAM

Probably one of the most apparently careless fliers in the early days of Alaska aviation was Harold ("Thrill 'em, Chill 'em, Spill 'em, No Killem") Gillam (FIG. 1-4). Harold would fly in any weather. He had the uncanny ability—not to mention nerve—to fly in the worst conceivable weather. When other Alaskan pilots were grounded because of bad weather, Gillam was in the air.

"Everybody loved Harold," the saying went around Cordova, "except maybe a few husbands." Gillam looked the part of the swashbuckler of the sky. Well proportioned and blessed with devastatingly good looks, he was also the hero of the younger set as well. A third-grade Native in Cordova, assigned to write a poem about his favorite person, penned five lines that stuck to Gillam like fog to the Thompson Pass:

He thrill 'em
Chill 'em
Spill 'em
But no killem
Gillam.

Reeve Museum

Fig. 1-4. *Harold ''Thrill 'em, Chill 'em, Spill 'em, no kill 'em'' Gillam.*

The son of an automobile salesman in Chadron, Nebraska, Gillam ran away from home at 16 and joined the Navy. He mustered out in 1923 and worked in Seattle for a while as a painter. Then he came north on a construction job to what was the end of the world in those days—Fairbanks, Territory of Alaska. When the project was finished, Gillam stayed on and took flying lessons.

Ironically, considering his career, Gillam was a survivor of Alaska's first fatal air crash. He was aboard a Swallow as a flying student when the plane suddenly spun out of control and crashed. The instructor was killed instantly. Gillam, with his wounds stitched, was out flying the next day. And it wasn't too long before he was practicing pulling out of spins—alone.

Gillam entered aviation in a money-making capacity in 1931 in the Copper Mining district inland from Cordova. From a pilot's point of view, the area was cursed. It had a steep mountain that was often blanketed by storm clouds from the Pacific. Turbulent air was more than common; it was more than frequent; it was expected. Fog was ever-present, winds were strong and unpredictable, and many of the landing strips were short and, quite literally, hacked out of the side of a mountain or on a plateau. "If you undershot," Oscar Winchell remembered with trepidation, "you ran into a bluff—when you took off you hadn't a foot to spare."

It was here that Gillam first made his name, but not without a few mishaps along the way. In his first six months of operation, Gillam had six crackups. No one was seriously injured, but he lost an estimated $30,000, which did not put him in good stead with his financial backers.

But Gillam proved early that he was a pilot with a future. He rapidly acquired a unique reputation. It appeared he could see in the dark and through clouds. On one particularly miserable night, for example, "Honest John" McCreary fell into a cellar and onto a nail. Since there was fear that McCreary would die without a doctor, Gillam flew the man 125 miles through a driving snow storm—at night—to Kennecott. There the doctor sadly predicted that McCreary would probably not last the night. Gillam went up again, this time flying to Cordova to bring back McCreary's son.

After three years in Cordova, Gillam headed north to Fairbanks again. With the money he had saved, Gillam bought a Pilgrim and began flying the Alaska Interior.

Here his reputation grew in size. Unlike other pilots, he would sleep during the day and fly at night, in any weather. Gillam would fly through pea soup fog without batting an eye. Cloud cover and darkness didn't bother him either. He would get up, dress, and fly.

One particular incident exemplifies what Gillam would do that other pilots refused to try. On a particularly miserable night, a large group of veteran bush pilots was grounded in McGrath. The storm was so fierce that, as one of the flyers stated, "I wouldn't have whipped a cat out there that night." Yet Gillam flew. The bush pilots were sitting around the fireplace in McGrath when they heard a plane come in. Gillam entered, said hello to his friends, refueled his plane, and took off. Three days later, those men were still there—and Gillam was back in Fairbanks safe and sound.

In 1938 Gillam was awarded the mail contract between Fairbanks and the 20 bush communities. Unlike Pan American, who had held the contract before, Gillam delivered his mail on time, month after month, with a perfect safety record. Gillam's record of delivery, according to the United States Postal Service, was the best in the United States or any of its territories.

While Alaskan bush pilots found Gillam's flying precision hard to believe, pilots from the Lower 48 didn't believe it at all. No one had eyes like that—or good luck that often. Hearing of Gillam's exploits, a pilot from United Airlines, Danneld Cathcart, wanted to see for himself. Bracing himself, he rode with Gillam from Fairbanks to Barrow.

Even under the best of conditions this was a treacherous route—the one on which Will Rogers and Wiley Post had been killed in 1935. It was a six-and-a-half-hour trip, and Gillam loaded enough fuel for seven hours. The men boarded the Pilgrim and Gillam went up, spiraled his way through several thousand feet of cover, and then proceeded to fly for six and a half hours over an unbroken sea of clouds. Suddenly Gillam nosed the plane down. Cathcart, undoubtedly sure that his last moments on earth were at hand, later recalled that once into the soup he saw nothing other than fog. The first objects he *did* see were antenna poles flashing by as Gillam landed on the Barrow lagoon.

Although every pilot in Alaska felt that he "hadn't a nerve in his body," it appears today that Gillam was not just flying by the seat of his pants. At a time when most pilots steered by compass alone, Gillam was a technology buff. He established air-ground radio stations in those areas where he flew frequently and had old-timers monitor them when he was in the area. He installed a direction-finder, directional gyro, altimeter, and artificial horizon in the plane and studied weather patterns assiduously.

Gillam's good luck was not to last, however. The Civil Aeronautics Board, forerunner of the Federal Aviation Administration, was not thrilled with his antics and filed charges against him numerous times for his "bizarre approaches" to landing strips. But before any action could be taken, Gillam took a flying job with Morrison-Knudsen. Flying passengers and cargo all over the Territory of Alaska, Gillam was putting in 125-hour work months, far in excess of the 100 maximum. On January 5, 1943, Gillam picked up five passengers in Seattle. A storm was headed in and after "considerable argument" Gillam was given permission to head north.

Four hours later Gillam entered dense fog in Southeast Alaska and proceeded to grope his way north. What he did not know was that the maps he had been given were obsolete. He became confused and began to circle at 6,000 feet trying to orient himself. Then his plane began icing. Suddenly an engine went out. The plane was hit with a powerful downdraft that dropped the plane 4,000 feet before he could recover. The next thing the passengers saw were mountainside and trees whizzing by. Gillam steered for a break in the clouds, but he was too low. One of the wings caught a tree top and the plane came down very hard.

Since Gillam had not bothered to use the radio to report his position, no one knew exactly where the plane had gone down. It would be more than a month before the survivors were located. Only then was it revealed that they were just 16 minutes by air from Ketchikan. Almost home free. One of the passengers had died, and the others had suffered horribly during the month. But Gillam was missing. After the plane crashed, Gillam, with just a gash on his head, had headed out to look for help. He had never returned. When his body was discovered, it was determined that he had tried to cross an ice-covered creek. The ice had not been thick enough to support his weight and he had tumbled into the ice water. Apparently he had taken his clothes off to dry and, in failing to start a fire, had frozen to death.

ARCHIE FERGUSON

He was Alaska's "Clown Prince," one of the Territory's most reknown bush pilots. It wasn't that he was a great pilot; rather, he had a personality that you could absorb, a laugh a minute. He was Archie Ferguson from Kotzebue, the Flying Clown, and he had a string of zany achievements to his name that would have made the Marx Brothers proud—and there were *three* of them!

Archie came to the Territory of Alaska with his parents in 1917 when his family opened up a trading post in the Kotzebue area. Universally described as gnarled and dumpy, he looked more like one of the seven dwarfs than a pilot in the swashbuckling mold of Harold Gillam or Bob Reeve. He was always looking for a laugh, and when he got one he joined in—and his laugh was unique, a cackle like Donald Duck! Always talking, always laughing, another bush pilot remarked that Archie would "fly 300 miles, ask 300 questions, answer them all himself, and fly 300 miles back." Other descriptions were accurate as well. "Maybe he's a pilot," a lot of bush pilots said of Ferguson, "but he shouldn't be."

Claiming to have had more crack-ups than any other pilot in Alaska, Ferguson ran the farthest north flying service under the American flag. His company was named Ferguson Airways and his motto was "Anywhere, Anytime." He meant it. Ferguson loved to fly. Even on those days when it was impossible for him to make a trip, he would clamber aboard his plane and fly in circles around Kotzebue. Asked why, Ferguson would often reply, "I dunno, somehow in a plane I feel differ'nt. I'd go nuts if I couldn't fly."

Ferguson's first trip in an airplane was with Noel Wien in 1926. Once aloft, Wien proceeded to scare the living daylights out of Archie by doing barrel rolls and loops and watched in amusement as the frightened Ferguson gripped the sidewalls of the plane in terror. But far from convincing him to stay on solid ground, the flight only sharpened Ferguson's desire to fly. Deciding to buy his own plane and to learn to fly, he spent $4,000 in 1931 for a Great Lakes Trainer and spent another thousand to get it to Kotzebue. Then he hired a trainer whose ad he saw in a magazine and had the man, Chet Browne of Colorado, come north (FIG. 1-5).

After 60 hours of training, seven times longer than was normally required, Ferguson was still not ready to solo. But he thought he was ready to solo. He wanted to solo. And by *&%, he was going to solo. Finally, Browne relented and let him go up. But, taking a page from Archie's book of practical jokes, he slipped an alarm clock under the pilot's seat. It was set to go off 10 minutes after takeoff.

"Go right up over town," advised Browne with a smile on his face. "Climb to a thousand feet and circle around, and be sure to take your time."

All went well for nine minutes and 59 seconds with Archie flying steadily. Then the alarm went off and the plane began wallowing across the sky, as if a wild man was

Brian Nelson

Fig. 1-5. *Pilot's decals are as individual as the pilots.*

in the cockpit—which one was. "Gosh I was scairt," Ferguson said later. "I thought it was some kind of a signal!" He managed to land safely but brought the plane down on a sandbar in the harbor rather than on the landing strip.

Ferguson's record with both cargo and passengers is replete with unique incidents and humorous anecdotes. Ferguson was infamous for monopolizing the air waves—even during the war years when radio silence was the established rule. Once a radio operator in Nome who was not familiar with Ferguson and his antics tried to get Archie to stay off the air. Ferguson began the conversation in his own inimitable style: "Nome Radio, Nome Radio. This is Cessna Two Zero Seven Six Six. Gosh it's startin' to rain up here! Looks like some awful dirty stuff ahead! Gimme yer weather in the clear!"

Mindful that the only authorized chatter on the radio was for an emergency, the operator asked innocently: "Cessna Two Zero Seven Six Six, do you declare this an emergency?"

"Yer darn right," snapped Ferguson into his microphone, "Any time I'm in the air it's an emergency!"

Along with being a pilot, Ferguson was a successful entrepreneur. He and his brother built a sawmill and several trading posts in the vicinity of Kotzebue. They also started and operated a mink farm, built and operated the first movie house north of the Arctic Circle, brought the first automobile (an International pickup) above the Circle, and imported the first cow and motorcycle (FIG. 1-6).

Brian Nelson

Fig. 1-6. *Flying is a family activity. Make certain that everyone knows what safety means and follows the rules.*

Ferguson's parents, incidentally, were frightened to death by the thought of Archie in a plane, and every time he approached their home in Shungnak they were known to look up in terror. Passengers also had these moments of terror. One winter his plane broke through the ice at Shungnak and several inches of wooden propeller were sheared off before he could get the plane ashore. Hefting an axe he hacked off a few inches of the undamaged end of the propeller while the passengers watched with incredulity. "I'll fix this baby," Ferguson said jovially, "We're really going to fly today!" It took the plane more than three miles of skipping along the ice "rattling like a sawmill" before it finally took off.

Once he was transporting a baby polar bear from Point Hope. The two had been aloft about 10 minutes when Archie became aware that the cub had gnawed through its bonds and was roaming around the back of his plane. Unfamiliar with an airplane, the cub began taking bites out of the pilot's seat and clawing at the fuselage. Finally, the bear settled down. As long as the flying was smooth there was no problem, but whenever there was turbulence, the bear became rambunctious.

Archie did make it down, and the polar bear cub, which later grew rather large, was a fixture in Kotzebue for years.

Fig. 1-7. *The bush pilot's Cadillac, a Turbo-Beaver.*

Brian Nelson

Ferguson's antics go on and on. One time he reported seeing a Japanese submarine moving north along the Arctic coast. Another time he took out 30 feet of telephone line and flew into Nome with the wire wrapped around his prop. On another occasion, while hunting wolves from his airplane, he became so excited he shot his own propeller off.

Archie Ferguson is probably best known today for what is called the "Arctic Bump." For Archie, there was no such thing as a trip without excitement, even if he had to create that excitement. Flying between Kotzebue and Nome, for instance, he had to cross the Arctic Circle. Whenever Ferguson crossed that theoretical line he would cut the gas to the engine.

"We're comin' ta the Arctic Circle!" he would shout as he reached for the gas line switch. "Ya can't see it but ya'll sure know when we hit it. The engine'll quit! There's no air in that darn circle for 800 feet!" Then he'd cut the gas line and the plane would go into a nose dive. Passengers would shriek and cry in terror until Archie opened the gas line and restarted the prop (FIG. 1-7).

Today, Alaska's pilots play this tidbit of heritage to the hilt. When crossing the Arctic Circle, Alaska Airlines pilots still "bump" their planes. Their home office keeps this legend alive as well. When reached for comment, Lou Cancelmi, Assistant Vice President of Communications for Alaskan Airlines, noted, with a straight face, that the rarified air above the Arctic Circle actually made flying smoother. "Because of the thicker air currents above the Circle," Cancelmi noted, "pilots are able to make more fluid, banking motions when landing. These are known as 'Arctic turns.' Used properly, these turns can save on fuel consumption."

The saga of the Alaska bush pilot is unique in the annals of American history. It was a two decade era, from 1930 to 1950, an odd time for a frontier. Short though it was, the era of the American cowboy was not much longer (FIG. 1-8).

Brian Nelson

Fig. 1-8. *One of the greatest rewards of being a bush pilot is the amount of territory you can cover, much of which is untouched by man. This is the Matanuska Glacier in Alaska.*

2
Reading the Weather Like a Book

WHEN YOU WERE YOUNG AND GULLIBLE, THERE WERE PEOPLE IN WHOM you placed great faith. You believed the man who advertised the toy that walked up the wall and across the ceiling, for instance. But when you bought the toy, well, it just didn't perform the way it was supposed to.

When you got older, of course, you had learned a bit. You were skeptical. You had learned that there is no such thing as a free lunch, that Santa Claus can't bring a Porsche down the chimney in a great white canvas bag, and that the only thing that's accurate in an evening weather report is what happened that day.

Unfortunately, an accurate weather report is an oxymoron. As a pilot, keep in mind that there is no such beast as an accurate weather report. Even the highly sophisticated aviation weather reports are only as good as when and where the data was collected. Unless you enjoy taking your life in your hands, take the weather report with a grain of salt.

One of the virtues of being a casual pilot is that most of the time you have the option of avoiding bad weather. Unless your life depends on it, it's not a good idea to fly in bad weather. Harold Gillam may have been able to fly in pea soup but, remember, it finally killed him.

As far as most pilots are concerned, it may not be possible to fly in good weather all the time. You might be coming back from hunting in Pan Am weather, crest a mountain range, and drop into another weather system. Suddenly the plane is being jerked violently from side to side, cargo is shifting in the fuselage, and your passengers' faces are as green as a St. Patrick's day shamrock. Then you ask yourself, "Was this trip really necessary?"

If you want to live to be an old pilot, learn to read the weather like a book. While you cannot see or predict every weather condition, you can steer clear of many hazardous situations simply by becoming weather wise. While this involves as much bookwork as practical experience, it will be worth your while in the long run. You will not avoid every hazardous situation, but you will certainly eliminate those into which you might otherwise be drawn because of ignorance.

ATMOSPHERIC STRUCTURE

Your first clue to reading weather like a book is to understand the structure of the atmosphere. It's important to understand that there is a difference between *air* and *atmosphere*. There is air in the atmosphere, but the term *atmosphere* means the composition and character of air at different altitudes. What we call air is actually a mixture of gases, three-quarters of it being nitrogen. Oxygen only makes up 21 percent, and trace gases make up the last one percent.

The atmosphere begins at ground level and extends upwards, with air getting thinner and thinner with each succeeding foot. The top zone, which has no air to speak of, is the ionosphere. It is roughly 300 miles off the surface of the earth and the only movement that is visible from earth in this zone is the aurora borealis.

The aurora, incidentally, is believed to be caused by a solar wind of ions that is focused through the van Allen belt. Though there are auroras during the daylight hours, only those at night are visible to the naked eye. The best possible place to see the aurora is Fort Yukon on the Arctic Circle. The University of Alaska, Fairbanks, has an observatory there that often sends rockets into the aurora to study the phenomenon. But if you go looking for the aurora, wear a jacket. It gets nippy, nippy, nippy in Fort Yukon on winter nights. You might want to take a tape recorder with you as well. The aurora will make a crackling sound as it ribbons across the sky.

Back to the structure of the atmosphere. The zone below the ionosphere is the stratosphere. Roughly 40 to 60 miles off the surface of the earth, the stratosphere is thin on air and thick on emptiness. It will only be at 45,000 to 65,000 feet that clouds will begin to form. This area is known as the troposphere. Interestingly, the troposphere is higher in the summer than in the winter because heat causes the air to expand and, on earth, it is highest over the equator for the same reason.

The water vapor content of the troposphere is known as weather. The more water vapor, the greater the chance of clouds forming and, eventually, rain falling. The chance of rain falling varies from area to area, thus the need for weather forecasters. Weather patterns also create and are in turn affected by winds and temperature gradients. Other factors that affect the weather are seasonal changes, temperature gradients, and sunspots.

The atmosphere is measured by pressure, and the standard unit of measurement is psi, pounds per square inch. But the increment value of atmospheric pressure is read as millibars. At sea level at 59°F the pressure of the atmosphere is about 15 pounds-per-square-inch, or 1013 millibars. Millibar readings are very important for pilots because altimeters read the altitude on the basis of sea level, not the relative altitude of the ground. In other words, if a plane is flying over the ocean at 3,000 feet, the altimeter will read 3,000 feet. If the same plane then flies over an island that has a 1,000-foot mountain range, as the plane passes over the range the altimeter will still read 3,000 feet.

Additionally, your altimeter will not always read 3,000 feet if you are flying at 3,000 feet. If there is a strong thermal updraft, your altimeter will read *lower* than you actually are. Conversely, if you are flying through a low pressure area, your altimeter will read *higher* than normal. To adjust for localized pressure systems where you will be flying, call the airport and ask for their *station pressure*. This is the millibar reading at that airport. Once you have set that reading into your altimeter, it will help you with takeoffs and landings at that airport.

Another factor that affects the weather, and flying, is the relative humidity. Water vapors begin as water, which should come as no surprise. As oceans, lakes, rivers, ponds, puddles, and spills evaporate, water in gaseous form rises. Air can retain water vapor, but its ability to do so depends on temperature.

On warm days, for instance, the air can hold more water vapors than on cold days. During the summer, humid days occur when the air is saturated with water vapors. The more vapor there is in the air, the higher the *relative humidity*. If the relative humidity approaches 100 percent, that means that the air is totally saturated.

However, as the temperature begins to drop, there is a *dew point*. This is the temperature at which water vapors will change from being an invisible gas to a cloud formation. After a humid day, as the temperature drops in the evening, you can see clouds begin to form. If the temperature continues to drop, the water vapors in the clouds condense. As more and more water vapors become liquid, the accumulating weight of the droplets becomes large enough to be attracted by gravity. Then there is rain. If the outside air temperature is within 4 °F of the dew point, fog or low clouds can occur.

Another atmospheric condition with which a pilot must contend is wind. Rather, it's winds (FIGS. 2-1, 2-2, and 2-3). That's because there is no consistent movement of air, even in the same tidal system. Air masses move, collide, meld, and pass around or by each other, often causing turbulence. Winds can be light and localized or they can be regional. They can be found at high altitude or on the ground only. There are also wind shears, gusts, blasts, tornadoes, hurricanes, and convection currents. All in all, these are terms that drive home the point that winds are not consistent.

While you cannot see the atmospheric processes at work, you can see the results of those processes. You cannot *see* the wind, for instance, but you can see the effect of the wind. Bending trees, blowing leaves, smoke leaving a chimney at an angle, or children being swept off their tricycles and bounced down the sidewalk are all indications that a wind is present. But the wind itself is invisible.

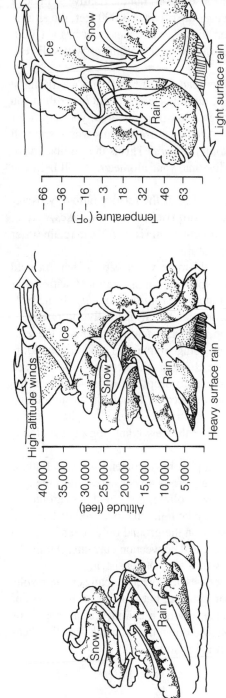

Temperature (°F)
63
46
32
18
−3
−16
−36
−66

Light surface rain

Rain

Snow

Ice

Fig. 2-3. *The drying stage. Mostly down drafts. Rain diminishing and not very rough though it might appear that you are flying into rough weather.*

Altitude (feet)
5,000
10,000
15,000
20,000
25,000
30,000
35,000
40,000

High altitude winds

Ice

Snow

Rain

Heavy surface rain

Fig. 2-2. *The mature state. Heavy rain, possibly hail, up and down drafts, air chopped up and rough.*

Snow

Rain

Fig. 2-1. *The early or building stage. Lots of updraft and very rough.*

20

CLOUDS

To read the weather like a book, first learn to be a cloud watcher. Not only will the cloud formations tell you direction and force of winds—and at what altitude the wind is blowing—but also if the winds are changing (FIG. 2-4). Clouds can tell you where it is raining as well as where it will probably rain and when. However, the study of clouds is not something you can do in an afternoon or by memorizing drawings in a Boy Scout Manual. It takes time.

Cloud types are divided into three basic groups: high, middle, and low altitude. At each of these altitudes there are three designations: streaked, layered, and heaped. With regard to vocabulary, rain-bearing clouds (dark) have the term *nimbus* attached to the end of the cloud type (FIG. 2-5). Heaped clouds that are about to dump rain, for instance, are cumulonimbus. But don't be dismayed at all the linguistic possibilities. Overall there are only about 10 distinctive cloud patterns with which to be concerned.

At high altitudes are the cirrus clouds (FIG. 2-6). This cloud formation is easy to identify. Just remember that in Latin *cirrus* means "streak." Ranging in altitude from 15,000 to 45,000 feet, these clouds appear as tiny scarves in the sky. Even though these clouds are composed of ice crystals, because they are so high, it is possible to have cirrus formations even on a hot summer day.

As far as the temperature of the atmosphere is concerned, the general rule of thumb is that there will be a 5.5 °F drop in temperature for each 1,000 feet of altitude. Thus, even if it is 100 °F on the ground, it is −150 °F at 45,000 feet: 5.5 °F per 1,000 feet times 45,000 feet less the initial 100 °F of ground temperature. However, be careful. Do not assume that the temperature always gets colder the higher you get. There can be temperature inversions, for instance, where it can be substantially warmer at 3,000 feet than at ground level.

Cirrus clouds are often harbingers of a storm. But if the thin wispy streaks in the sky are all you can see, the storm could be a thousand miles away. As the storm front moves closer, the cirrus clouds will grow from barely visible wisps to quite visible streaks. They will also descend to the 30,000 foot range, where they are known as *cirrostratus clouds*.

Often the cirrostratus clouds will blanket the sky. Because they are composed of ice crystals it is not uncommon to see a rainbow-like halo around the sun or moon. In Alaska, this is called a *sundog*. During the winter, weather conditions might obscure part of the halo, leaving the viewer on the ground with the impression that the sundogs are rainbow-like pillars that stand on either side of the sun. Rings of light around the moon—obviously at night—are said to be a sure sign of rain. While the rings are an indicator that there is moisture in the air, it is not a sure sign that a storm in imminent. Furthermore, in many parts of the country, the cirrostratus clouds take on the familiar shape of an anvil in advance of a thunderstorm. This is a strong indication that there will be lightning.

At slightly lower altitudes, about 25,000 feet, but still above the freezing level, the cirrus formations begin to form into cirrocumulus clouds (FIG. 2-7). These look like giant fish scales; hence, the name *mackerel sky*.

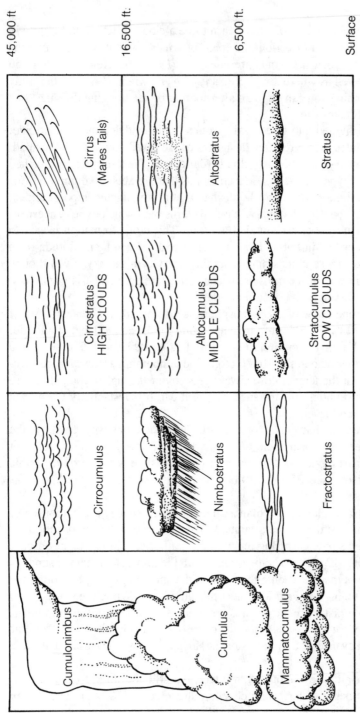

45,000 ft

16,500 ft.

6,500 ft.

Surface

Cirrus
(Mares Tails)

Altostratus

Stratus

Cirrostratus
HIGH CLOUDS

Altocumulus
MIDDLE CLOUDS

Stratocumulus
LOW CLOUDS

Cirrocumulus

Nimbostratus

Fractostratus

Cumulonimbus

Cumulus

Mammatocumulus

Fig. 2-4. Cloud height and classification.

22

Fig. 2-5. *Nimbostratus: a grey or dark massive cloud layer, diffused by more or less continuous rain, snow, or sleet.*

Fig. 2-6. *Cirrus clouds: thin, white feather-like clouds in patches or narrow bands; composed entirely of ice crystals of varying size. Larger crystals often trail down in well-defined wisps called "mare's tails."*

Easily confused with the lowest of the cirrus formations are the highest of the altocumulus clouds. The primary difference, though it can be subtle, is that the altocumulus are puffy as opposed to the cirrocumulus, which are streaked. The altocumulus appear at the 20,000-to-25,000-foot range and are composed almost entirely of water droplets.

Fig. 2-7. Cumulus clouds: detached domes or towers that are usually dense and well-defined. The clouds develop vertically in the form of rising mounds of which the bulging upper part often resembles cauliflowers. These clouds are often referred to as "Cu" by pilots. They are composed of a great density of small water droplets. Larger drops develop within the clouds and eventually fall as rain. Ice crystals often form in the upper portion. Cumulus clouds frequently develop in the afternoon over land, and during the night over water.

The lowest level of clouds, between 5,000 and 20,000 feet, falls into three categories. The first of these is the *cumulus*, best recognized as the traditional, fluffy clouds. Often called "fair weather clouds," they are formed by extensive amounts of water vapor gathered by the heating of land or water. Tiny water particles caught in the upward movement of heat, known as *thermals*, rise until the moisture condenses into clouds. Individual cumulus clouds do not last very long, sometimes only as long as 10 or 15 minutes. But as long as the thermals are present, more and larger cumulus clouds will appear. They often disappear at sunset.

However, if the atmosphere is unstable the cumulus clouds may not disappear. Rather, they may grow larger and larger, darker and darker, to become cumulonimbus or storm clouds. From this cloud formation will come rain, sometimes lightning and hail. What is noticeable about these clouds, particularly from the point of view of a pilot, is the height of the cumulonimbus. Vertical growth to 50,000 feet is not uncommon.

The other two low-level clouds are *stratus* and *stratocumulus*. The difference between the two is their shape. The stratus clouds are well known to pilots because they form what is called a low deck or, to pilots, a ceiling. The stratus clouds will completely obscure the sun and indicate, quite clearly, that a storm is coming very soon. When it is raining or snowing, these clouds are called *nimbostratus*. Puffier stratus clouds are known as *stratocumulus*. At very low levels, stratus clouds are known as *fog*.

By watching the clouds you can see what kind of weather you are flying into. If you take off from Anchorage and there are cirrostratus clouds that gradually turn to cumulonimbus formations as you progress toward Fairbanks, chances are very good you are flying into a storm. If you see a cloud that apparently has a side or bottom shaved flat, that's a good indication that there is wind in the area of the cloud at the altitude where the shearing has taken place. If you are flying over a mountain range and see clouds spilling from one side of the crest line to the other, you are in for some rough flying as you top the spine of the range.

More important for the casual flyer, if you see large cumulus clouds, that's an indication that there are thermal updrafts. What is important to keep in mind is that these thermal updrafts are not even. As you fly over fields, roads, lakes, and rivers, the thermals will be different. This is particularly important to understand if you are landing. On a hot day, should you be descending to land over a lake, then a roadway, and then a plowed field, you will find that the different thermal gradients will give you a bumpy descent. For a smooth landing, count on the thermals being there, prepare for them, and then adjust your descent accordingly.

If you are flying near a large body of water, it's important to remember that you will most likely have onshore breezes during the day. Air, heated by earth re-radiation of the sun's energy, will rise over land and cool as it crosses the large body of water. As it cools it falls, moving the air over the water toward the land and creating an onshore breeze.

In the evening and night, this process is reversed. Since water retains heat longer than the earth does, the earth will cool faster than the large body of water. Thus the air over the land will cool faster than that over water. Since the air over the large body of water is warmer, it rises and will cool when it passes over the land. This system will produce an offshore breeze, one that blows out over the water.

For scientific purposes, both these atmospheric cycles are caused by pressure systems. *High pressure* occurs when a blanket of air is falling to earth. Conversely, *low pressure* means that air is warm and rising.

HIGHS AND LOWS

Weather systems move, so to speak, as the result of highs and lows (FIG. 2-8). To understand how highs and lows work, imagine pouring some honey on a tabletop. The moment the honey hits the table, it starts to spread in a platter moving slowly in all directions at the same time. If you stop pouring, the pancake of honey will continue to grow in area but will also grow progressively thinner.

Pressure systems build in much the same way, but instead of honey, the pressure system will be of air. Since warm air rises in thermal currents, cold air must descend to the earth in much the same manner as the honey being poured from a container. Air

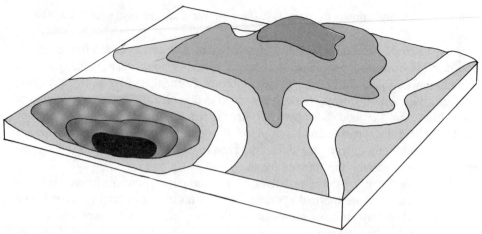

Fig. 2-8. *Low pressure is like a hole in the sky, often called a depression. High pressure is like a hill. High pressure moves slowly. Low pressure, called lows, move faster but have to go around highs or push them out of the way.*

is forced down, making it identifiable to a *barometer*, an instrument that measures air pressure.

Unlike the honey, however, air masses have both movement and motion. Not only can they move from place to place, but they have internal gyrations as well. Because of the *Coriolis force*, winds will move in a clockwise direction in the northern hemisphere. If you are flying in Australia, expect the winds in their weather systems to circulate in the opposite direction.

Obviously, if you are watching a barometer and see the pressure decrease, that means that a low pressure area has moved into your neck of the woods. Why is this important? Because when cold, low pressure fronts meet moisture-laden warm pressure fronts, condensation occurs. In other words, the ability of the air to hold onto its water vapor is decreased. The colder the invading air mass, the less ability the mixed air will have to hold vapor. This, in turn, means rain in the summer or snow in the winter.

If the pressure system is large enough, it will also mean winds (FIG. 2-9). If it is stronger still, it means storms. Pressure systems larger and stronger still mean you should not be flying anywhere except into your basement.

Pressure systems can be so small that they occur just over a handful of acres. Or they can be so large that they cover entire sections of the United States. For a good idea as to the size of some of the fronts, just watch your television during the national news.

From a global standpoint, weather professionals view the earth as having *three-cell circulation*. The first cell begins at the equator and extends to 30 degrees above and below the equator. Because the equator is so warm, air masses rise into the atmosphere. This air has no option but to move north and south and to extend in that direc-

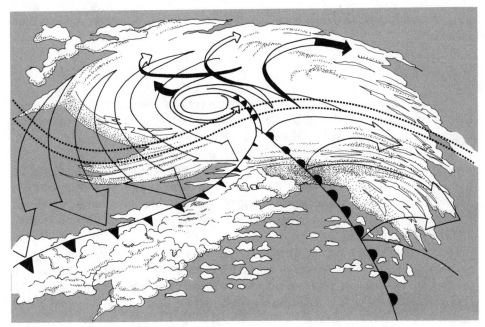

Fig. 2-9. *A weather system on the move.*

tion until it cools enough to descend. This cooling is identifiable at 30 degrees north and south, which is where the mass descends.

The second cell begins at 30 degrees north and south and extends to 60 degrees latitude in both hemispheres. Here there are belts of prevailing winds, usually westerly winds. The air masses mix, causing winds and storms whose intensity will vary with the season.

The third cell is from 60 degrees north and south to the poles. At about 60 degrees north and south, very cold air from the poles will meet with warm air masses moving toward the poles. Where the masses meet and form a vertical column they create a permanent zone of low pressure.

Pressure gradients can be identified on a map with the use of *isobars*, the concentric lines that indicate areas where pressure is building or diminishing. *Weather fronts*, which are basically changes in meteorological pressure along a wide front, are most commonly known as "the lines with the triangles and bumps that you see each evening on the weather map." Warm fronts have semicircles on the line, while cold fronts have triangles. The fronts will move in the way in which the semicircles and triangles appear to be pulling them.

On a more localized level, mountain ranges break the movement of pressure fronts. Fronts collide with one another and cause cyclones. Updrafts and thermals can alter the impact of the fronts. Since such a wide variety of regional factors can affect the movement of high pressure fronts, it takes a Ph.D. in climatology to interpret them all. Fortunately, when it comes to predicting the weather, that is exactly why it is done by a Ph.D.

WIND

It's also important to note that winds blow in circular patterns, parallel to the isobar markings. These winds will be affected by a number of conditions, two of the most important being gravity and friction.

Because the force of gravity works on all molecules on earth, it will affect the wind. The downward attraction of gravity will cause the wind to thicken at its base. Then friction will cause the wind to slow. As the wind rushes through forests and around buildings and slams against immovable objects, its speed will be slowed. Because of ground frictions, the speed of the wind will be affected all the way up to 2,000 or 3,000 feet AGL.

Friction will also affect the direction of the wind. Even though you cannot see it, the wind rotates. However, friction against the earth causes the wind to flow against the contours of the isobar at an angle of about 30 degrees toward the center of the high pressure system. What this means to a pilot is that the direction of the wind will be different 3,000 feet aloft than it is at ground level.

When flying in the bush, it is extremely important to be prepared for wind. Air movement patterns change from one side of the mountain range to the next, from valley to meadow, and from one bend in the river to the next. Unexpected crosswinds can lead a pilot to over-correct—or under-correct. If an unexpected crosswind is severe, it is called a *shear*, or a *wind shear*. While the wind shear at ground level during landing or takeoff is the most deadly, there are high altitude shears. Usually these occur when there are temperature inversions, when temperatures are colder on the ground than they are at higher altitudes.

Since temperature and moisture are so closely related to atmospheric instability, some pilots feel that if they are flying in clear skies with stable temperatures that there is no problem with turbulence. This is an error. There is such a beast as *clear air turbulence* (*CAT*) that can appear anywhere. It cannot be predicted, but it can be expected.

The best advice for dealing with winds is to use common sense. Keep a sharp eye on the wind sock. Before landing and taking off, look at trees or bushes near the runway to see if there is movement different from the wind sock. When in the air, keep an eye on your instruments. If you are going at full speed but only registering 25 miles an hour, that's a pretty good indication that you are fighting a head wind. Use your instruments, not just your eyes.

WINTER WEATHER

While it is very easy to talk about the weather during the summer, winter is an entirely different story. The earth is colder, substantially reducing warm thermals.

The days get shorter so there is less sunshine warming the earth. This also means there is less re-radiation of the atmosphere from the earth.

This, in turn, decreases the amount of heat in the atmosphere, which reduces the air's ability to retain water vapor. What does this mean in small words? It means rain and snow. Lots of both.

But just because there is less moisture in the atmosphere does not mean there is none at all. There is and, in the winter, that moisture can be very dangerous. Often there will be a *temperature inversion*, an atmospheric condition where the temperature on the surface of the earth is substantially colder than at 2,000 or 3,000 feet. If temperatures at lower levels are below freezing while the temperatures at higher levels are above freezing, icing can occur if you fly through rain. For instance, if you are flying through rain at 3,000 feet and the temperature is 36 °F and the thermometer reads 30 °F on the ground, the water that is collecting on your plane will freeze as you descend. Worse, once you descend below freezing altitude, rain will hit your plane and freeze on its fuselage. Your lift will be reduced, your weight increased, your forward motion slowed, and your drag increased. If you remain in these conditions for very long, more than a matter of minutes, you may find that your airspeed is so reduced that you have to come down a lot sooner than you expected.

The best advice for pilots who are considering flying in icing conditions is very simple: don't. If you don't have to take the risk, don't. If you are already up when you encounter icing, stay above the freezing gradient until just before you start your descent to land. Remember, once you are into the freezing zone you will have about five minutes of grace before you have real problems. By then your plane will be about 1,000 pounds heavier and very difficult to maneuver.

Hail also occurs when there is a temperature inversion. The difference, however, is that there are strong winds associated with the formation of hailstones. Imagine a strong wind flowing at 3,000 feet coupled with an inversion where freezing is above 3,000 feet. Water droplets will form and fall as rain. As they enter the layers of air where the temperature is below freezing, the droplets become ice. But these little ice balls are very light and when they hit the layer of wind, they are tossed back up into the atmosphere.

When the tiny balls of ice pass back into the layer that is above freezing, water droplets will cling to the ice, making the droplets heavier. Then the force of gravity takes over and the enlarged balls of ice drop until they hit the layer of wind. Tossed up again and again, the tiny balls of ice grow in size until their weight allows them to pass through the band of wind and fall to the ground as chunks of ice, the size of those ice balls depending primarily on the speed of the wind.

Flying through any hailstorm is dangerous. Not all hailstones are the size of peas. Some of those ice chunks can be as large as golf balls. When they hit they can do massive structural damage. Do not be fooled by weather conditions. Hail can fall up to 10 miles away from where it was created.

The best way to avoid problems with hail is to stay at least 20 miles away from any storms. In many cases, you can see a hailstorm coming. Should you spot a dark nimbus cloud with none of the telltale streamers reaching to earth, that is a clear indication that a hailstorm is on its way. You can also expect turbulence in the area and, if you fly into the belt of wind that is tossing those tiny balls of ice back up into the atmosphere, you could get the ride of your life.

Another winter weather problem is whiteout. While there are many definitions of the term, technically a whiteout exists any time the horizon and the ground blend together. Usually it happens when there is a uniform layer of clouds covering a white landscape. As the rays of the sun pass through the clouds, they are splintered and diffused and therefore strike the white terrain at all different angles. In effect, the scattering of light removes all shadows, and the horizon and sky appear as a single, composite, unbroken world of greyish white.

What this means to the pilot is that the horizon cannot be distinguished from the clouds. It would be, in the words of Joe Crosson in describing the weather in the famous search for Carl Ben Eielson, "like flying in a milk bottle." In whiteout conditions you can fly into mountains without even knowing they are there.

ALEUTIANS

Then there are the Aleutians. The Aleutians are an extremely dangerous place to fly. Weather conditions can change drastically over a period of minutes. In fact, the weather of the Aleutians is so unusual that there is even a specific term to define the unique winds that are characteristic of the islands. It's called a *williwaw*: a sudden, violent storm that rises from calm skies.

Stories of weather in the Aleutians are so bizarre that few pilots from the Lower 48 would believe them. At Cold Bay, it is common to have two winds, each blowing at 50 miles an hour, but in opposite directions at either end of the runway. Planes have to bank into the wind as they initiate takeoff and complete lift-off banked 90 degrees from where they started. Richard Reeve, President of Reeve Aleutian Airlines, remembers more than one time when he has had to land at an airstrip with three wind socks: "one blowing one way, the second another way, and the third showing dead calm."

The Aleutians, incidentally, have such unpredictable weather because they are the division between the cold waters of the Bering Sea and the warm Pacific Ocean. With the Japanese current washing the south side of the chain and the turbulent winds of the Bering on the north, the colliding air masses form storm clouds. Snow is not uncommon and high winds should be expected.

If you have the slightest inkling to fly in the Aleutians, read Brian Garfield's classic work *The Thousand Mile War*. During the Second World War, the Japanese captured the last two islands of the Aleutian Chain: Kiska and Attu. The United States military built bases along the Aleutians to stop the Japanese advance and opened up a war zone 1,000 miles long; hence, the title of the book.

Eventually, the United States Army invaded Attu. In the second bloodiest battle of the Pacific Theater, Attu was taken from the Japanese but not after staggering losses from a suicide charge on May 29, 1943. Of the 2,400 Japanese on Attu, there were only 28 prisoners, none of them officers.

If you are planning on flying in the Aleutians, talk to some of the seasoned bush pilots first. This is not a trip to take without extensive preparation. Other than the winds, there are also fog and rain, rain, rain, rain unlike that which you have ever seen before.

Also keep in mind that the Aleutian chain is volcanic in origin. This means that the beaches and landing strips are black. Expect your landings to be difficult. If you do not know exactly where you expect to land, you will have a hard time seeing the strip. There are a few paved runways but most of them are on military installations and will require permission and a security clearance. Some of the islands are also parks where you will need permission from the state or federal park service to camp. Stay away from Amchitka at all costs. An atomic bomb was tested there and although the authorities claim that there is no danger of radiation exposure, stay on the safe side.

As far as the vegetation of the Aleutians is concerned, there is a woman behind every tree. That's because there are no trees. Actually there are about six, in the Adak National Forest. The rest of the vegetation is about waist-high.

If you fly to Unimak Island, you will see some tall animals, however. These animals are known as brown bears and they can tip the scales at 1,600 pounds. While they do not eat humans, or, for that matter, attack humans, they do take a very dim view of being surprised or having someone upset their dinner. While there are no bears beyond Unimak Island, there are no caribou either. If you are planning a hunting trip to Unimak Island, be sure to read up on bears *before* you take off (FIG. 2-10).

Brian Nelson

Fig. 2-10. *Never trust that the weather will remain unchanged at your destination. While it might have been clear when you took off, an hour later your destination could be socked in. Monitor your local weather reports and don't take any chances.*

3
Cold Weather Flying

COLD WEATHER FLYING IS ONE OF THE JOYS THAT ALASKAN PILOTS HAVE over many pilots in the Lower 48. Alaskan pilots love to fly in the winter. That's because they don't have a choice. If you love to fly and you live in Alaska, you had better get used to flying in the winter.

Cold weather flying, however, is not "just like flying in warm weather but colder." In Alaska, it can get quite a bit colder. Colder than you can imagine. In the winter of 1988, for example, the Alaskan bush received the coldest temperatures ever recorded, −83°F—and that wasn't on the shady side of the igloo in a snow storm in January either. But pilots flew in those temperatures. Fuel and food had to move into remote villages and seriously ill or injured people had to come out. The bush pilots who ran those services, to this day, have nothing but horror stories to tell.

Cold weather flying requires some added skills. However, these skills cannot be picked up by flying occasionally or casually in cold weather. Flying in frigid temperatures divides the men from the boys very quickly, if you will excuse the sexist pun. It can be very dangerous, particularly if you think you can pick up everything you need to know "as you go along."

The best advice for learning to cold weather fly is to spend some time with a pilot who has done a lot of this kind of flying. It is not for amateurs. But you have a choice. You can learn from someone who has already made all the mistakes and is still alive or you can learn on your own, make all your own mistakes, lose a few airplanes, and then—if you're still alive—you can be an experienced cold weather flyer.

Immediately after filing a flight plan, the next most important step in cold weather flying is doing a good preflight check. "It's more than just a damn good preflight," Alaskan winter pilots say, "it's a *DAMN GOOD* preflight."

While it is hard to believe that someone reading this book would not know what a good preflight checkup would include, a comprehensive list of items is included for your use. This, incidentally, is a checklist used by Sound Adventures, a bush pilot service in Anchorage with six pilots. The lead pilot is Jim O'Meara, one of the authors of this book, with more than 14,000 hours of Alaska flying experience, winter and summer.

Don't take anything for granted. Do not whip through the preflight check as if it is just something to get done. Be meticulous. Take your time. What you don't know can kill you. Check everything carefully. The life you save, after all, will be your own.

KEEPING WARM

Warm everything up. Unless you really know what you are doing, don't jury-rig a heater. Buy a commercial one. There are a great number of engine warmers on the market, so shop around. Many of them are fine, but there are some that are as worthless as a moose pecan (FIG. 3-1). Buy on the basis of quality, not price. Don't expect to be able to warm your plane up with a heater that puts out fewer BTUs than a Coleman stove. That would be like trying to melt a pot of ice with a candle.

If you are not sure which heater to buy, check the back issues of flying magazines. Most journals have sections that rate products. If your local library doesn't have a magazine index, pull the fall and early winter issues. That's when the warmers are most likely to be covered. You should also ask around. What are other pilots using? When did they buy their warmers? What kind of trouble have they had?

If you are in the market for a heater, be sure to check out the Tannis Preheat Systems, which have a good name in the "heating biz." Located in Minnesota, Tannis has a wide variety of kits for different engines. Their preheaters are installed and, while they heat the entire engine, they operate off a plug.

Many commuter air couriers like the 115-volt plug-ins because they can be left on continuously—right until the plane leaves. Another plug-in model that is used widely by Alaskan pilots is the engine cylinder probe heaters. These require 115 volts and can also be left on continuously until the plane is ready to take off. This model will take a mechanic to install, as the probe becomes a part of the engine. Plug-ins are great—as long as you are within an extension-cord length of a plug in.

Also available on the market are electrical heating pads. Available in gradients from 50 to 300 watts, they install in minutes in the bottom of the oil pan and will heat 12 quarts of oil from −40°F to +60°F in about an hour. The 150 watt model is usually best for the 0-290 and up Lycoming and C-145 and up Continental engines.

When there is no electricity available, there are propane heaters that put out up to 50,000 BTUs (FIGS. 3-2 and 3-3). These put out enough heat to even unfreeze door locks and de-ice some of the aircraft.

Brian Nelson

Fig. 3-1. *An electric or battery-operated heater is serviceable as long as the temperature is not well below zero.*

Fig. 3-2. *An engine cover with the engine heating.*

Fig. 3-3. *In cold weather you will need to heat the aircraft engine. This is a propane heater working overtime in the deep snow of Alaska.*

And, if you are having *real* problems with the weather, you can go for the grand-daddy of heaters. Aerotech International of Winnipeg produces the BT400-42, a portable heater that puts out a wholloping 400,000 BTUs. Widely used by military, airlines, and commercial construction companies, this model is large enough (300 pounds) that it comes with its own trailer.

Once you've bought the best possible heater, try it out before you take it to your plane. Can you start it easily? If not, why not? Do not take the heater out to your plane until you are sure that it will work under real conditions.

It is also a good idea to play it safe. Even if you are sure that you will have no problem with your heater, keep a fire extinguisher handy. Some of the smaller ones cost under $20, and that's a low cost compared to the damage that fire can do to your plane. You should have a fire extinguisher on board anyway. Leave that one in place. Have an extra around just in case you need it.

While your engine is heating, sweep all the snow off the plane, particularly around the gas cap, or you could get water in your fuel. Water is heavier than fuel and will sink to the bottom of your gas tank. That means it will be the first liquid through your fuel line and will cause your engine to cough and possibly die.

Don't forget to clean off all the surfaces and wires (FIGS. 3-4, 3-5, 3-6, and 3-7). Particularly important are the areas between the air frame and flight control surfaces.

Figures 3-4, 3-5, and 3-6. *Proper cleaning of the snow from your airplane is not something you can do casually. Use a broom and a ladder. There's a lot of effort involved and you can place yourself and your passengers in danger if you try to cut the process short.* Brian Nelson

Brian Nelson

Fig. 3-5.

Brian Nelson

Fig. 3-6.

Brian Nelson

Fig. 3-7. *Heavy snow on a plane's wing may take quite a while to remove.*

Snow left in crevices can cause you to lose some control, which is not conducive to safe flying. Make sure that you test your ailerons, elevators, trim tabs, and rudder to make sure the cables and flight surfaces are free and clear (FIG. 3-8).

Do a visual inspection of your cables. How do they look? If they appear old or corroded, replace them. If they look serviceable, look for any broken strands, a sure sign of wear. Since you can't always detect broken strands easily, wrap a cloth around the steel wiring, squeeze it, and pull it down the length of your cable. You will be able to feel the broken ends as they snag the cloth. Other barely visible breaks in cable strands will be visible when you remove the cloth. The sharp ends often have snagged threads, making the breaks easy to identify.

Antenna wires are easy to forget, particularly if they are under the fuselage (FIG. 3-9). As you are sweeping those surfaces clear, make sure you are very careful when you are around your emergency locater transmitter (ELT) antenna. It does not stand much higher than the fuselage and is easy to snap off if you are not careful. While the loss of your ELT antenna will not affect the performance of your plane in the air, it will affect the range of your transmitter if you have an accident. That will affect your personal safety. After you have finished sweeping off your aircraft, make certain that your ELT antenna has not been damaged.

Fig. 3-8. *Check all moving parts on your plane before you take off. Ice and snow build-up between the control surfaces can cause you problems once you are aloft.*

Fig. 3-9. *Be careful of your ELT antenna when scraping snow off your aircraft.*

While heating your engine, be particularly conscious of your engine's oil. One of the problems that many pilots discover too late is that for all the heating they thought they did, their oil is still frozen. In many cases, this occurs because the oil is not completely thawed before the plane takes off. A pilot will heat the engine and then check the fluidity of the oil with the dipstick. When the oil on the dipstick is fluid, the pilot erroneously assumes that all the oil in the crankcase is fluid.

For a better understanding of what is happening in the engine, imagine a sealed jar full of ice. If you were to immerse that jar in a sink full of hot water, the ice would start to melt from the outside. Soon there would be a sheen of water on the inside of the glass and, the longer the jar remained in the hot water, the less ice there would be inside the jar. But if you did not heat the jar long enough, there would still be a block of ice floating in the liquid.

Frozen oil in an engine reacts to heat in the same way. It also thaws from the outside. It will take a while for the heat to liquefy the engine oil. If the engine is not heated long enough, the oil will not totally liquefy. Unfortunately, on many planes there is no way to know for sure if the oil is liquid. Using the dipstick will only tell you that there is oil on the level that the dipstick reaches. It will not tell you what is happening in the center of the pool of oil. If a pilot trusts the dipstick, he or she is *assuming* that all the oil in the crankcase has been thawed. This could be a very costly mistake.

Before taking off, make absolutely sure the oil is working properly. Don't guess; make certain. Don't assume that it will heat up once you get off the ground and the engine is running. The crankshaft doesn't know you are putting heat on it. It just warms up as the oil warms up. At −40°F, oil can freeze solid, hard enough for you to walk on it without leaving a scratch. It is impossible for oil of this consistency to be splashed onto the moving parts of the engine.

Once you have warmed the engine with a heater, start the engine. Does it start easily? If not, let it warm for a while longer. Once you can get it started easily, let it run for a while. Allow the engine to heat itself. Then, after it has warmed up, turn it off. Let it sit for a while, maybe 15 minutes, then crank it up again. Many pilots would not think of stopping the engine after it has been started. But think about it. When you go up in that plane you want to be absolutely sure that if the engine quits it will restart.

The cold weather is also going to affect your fuel, so plan your trips carefully. If the temperature is −30°F or colder, you are going to have problems with Jet A, which is basically 100 percent kerosene. It will congeal and cause you a world of problems. When the temperature gets that cold, switch to Jet B, which has lighter fuel added. That should take you down to −50°F, but when it gets that cold you shouldn't be flying at all.

One more note about flying in extremely cold weather. Don't shock your engine with the cold air. As you ease off the power, particularly as you are easing down for a landing, do it slowly. If you pull back too fast, you're going to get a rush of very cold air. This will cause the outside of your engine to cool faster than the inside, and the expansion differential will squeeze the pistons and other working parts. The engine won't like that and you could end up with a cracked cylinder. This is particularly true for turbo-charged engines. That's very expensive. Ease the throttle back; don't jerk it.

De-icing boots and hot props are good for VFR but not necessarily cost effective. For IFR flying, however, they are a must for cold weather flying. You are going to need them.

One of the cold weather adaptions I have found that works is running the oil lines right alongside the exhaust system. The oil lines are metal, so there's not a problem with any plastic or rubber burning. It's also a good idea to frequently check your hoses, clamps, seals, and battery. Very cold weather can affect them adversely.

Struts can also be a problem. What gives them their bounce is nitrogen that's compressed within the telescoping tubes. As the temperature drops, the pressure within the strut is reduced. The colder it gets, the less pressure there is. If it gets very cold, you might not have any bounce left in the struts at all. This means that your landings will be hard and that you stand a good chance of damaging your landing gear. Or the propeller might be so close to the ground that it can pick up small objects such as gravel or sand and throw them backwards causing damage to the plane. Checking the bolts on your skis is not a bad idea.

FUEL

Don't trust your tank gauges either. Check your tank visually. You don't know and the manufacturer cannot predict what your equipment will do under very cold conditions.

You can never go wrong testing your fuel either. Spend the time and the few dollars necessary to make sure that the fuel you have is fuel you can use. I carry a chamois with me to use as a filter in those places where I am not absolutely sure that fuel is filtered. I field-test my fuel by draining some into a glass to see if there is any water or other substance floating on top. I also smell it. If it smells "varnishy" or different than I would expect, I don't use the fuel. This may sound odd to a lot of pilots in the Lower 48 who just fuel up and go, but in many remote places there is not a lot of quality control on the fuel. Take your time and field-test the fuel. You want to know that there is something wrong with the fuel while you are on the ground, not up in the air.

TIEDOWNS

A word about tiedowns is also in order. Use them in the winter (FIG. 3-10). Use them on the ice even if you don't think you'll need them. If a wind comes up, you could find that your plane has blown across a lake. Under the best of circumstances, you'll have a hike to get to your plane. Under the worst of circumstances, you'll find that you don't have to drill a hole to go ice fishing; your plane has already done it for you.

It's also a good idea to check your plane throughout the winter even if you are not planning to use it. Occasionally, when the snow is heavy, build-up on the tail can cause a tri-gear plane to tilt back and lift the nose wheel off the ground. While this will usu-

Fig. 3-10. *Though many tiedowns appear to be unusual, they do the job.*

ally not damage the plane, it does place the plane in a position of risk if there is a wind. Tilted back, there is more surface for the wind to catch and thus a greater chance of catching the wind.

Over the years I have seen people do a lot of things to keep their planes safe during the winter when they do not fly them. Wrapping planes in plastic sheets and taping the sheets to form a tight fitting shroud is fine as long as you check the plane occasionally, particularly before a storm (FIG. 3-11). If your tape comes loose and the wind can find its way into the shroud, you could find that your plastic acts as a sail rather than as a sheet of protection.

Brian Nelson

Fig. 3-11. *Bush planes snowed in, probably for the winter.*

I have seen people shoveling out their tiedown area and, if you want to spend the time doing that, fine. I don't think that does very much but if it makes you feel good, fine, do it.

There are a couple of winter do's that I would recommend. I've seen a lot of people slide 2 × 4s under the fronts of their skis (FIG. 3-12). This raises the front portion of the skis off the snow and ice. Then, as you are warming up your plane, you can stand on the front portion of the skis and lever the backs up off the snow. This makes it substantially easier to break the skis free of the ice of the lake.

I've also found another use for 2 × 4s in the winter. When the lake finally freezes thick enough that I can land on it, I drill two holes in the ice where I want my tiedowns to be. Then I take a three-foot 2 × 4, tie one end of a 20-foot rope to it, and lever it under the ice. When the ice refreezes, I have a tiedown that is anchored in 1 foot of solid ice.

Brian Nelson

Fig. 3-12. *Note the 2 x 4 to keep the ski from freezing into the snow. Because of leverage, if the back of the ski should freeze to the ground, the pilot can stand on the front and snap the back free.*

Finding the tiedowns is easy as long as there are no snow storms. Just before I auger my tiedown holes I usually find a small spruce, about three feet tall. Then I put the base of the tree in the same hole as one of the tiedowns. When the tree freezes in, I have a marker that can be seen three feet above the level of the ice. If it snows, I can still find those tiedowns. I might have to dig around for 10 or 15 minutes, mind you, but I can still find the ropes. And, if the plane slips on the snow a bit and I hit the spruce, the tree just bends.

Wing covers are also a must for cold weather flying (FIGS. 3-13 and 3-14). They protect your wings and mean a lot less work for you when you go to sweep off the plane. In my experience, the most popular colors are green and red, both of which show up well against the white background of snow. However, the next set of wing covers I buy will be fluorescent. During the spring, summer, and fall, I'll leave them in the plane. They don't take up that much space and in an emergency I can spread them out on the ground as a visual signal as to where I am. When the snow is gone and the ground is brown or green, those wing covers will show up like a moose in a bath-tub.

If you are going to be away from your plane for more than a few hours, get it off the ice. More than one Alaskan pilot has put his or her plane on skis, tied it down, and then left for a month. During that time, a chinook came through the area, the tempera-ture went up, a sheen of water appeared on the ice, and the plane's skis were

Fig. 3-13. *See how the wing covers have provided protection to the wing's surface. Because of the wing covers, snow and ice have had little opportunity to accumulate while the plane has been on the ground.*

Fig. 3-14. *Take your time getting your plane ready to go in very cold weather.*

47

immersed in the water. The chinook passed, the temperature dropped, and the plane became frozen in the ice. Unless that pilot has a blow torch or an axe, that plane is going to stay in that position for quite a while.

Since freezing to the ground is always a possibility in the winter, I always shake my plane loose before I taxi out—even if I have only been away for a few minutes. This procedure is as simple as going out to the end of each wing and giving it a gentle but firm rocking. I do both sides, just to be sure. If there is any freezing, this breaks the plane free.

EMERGENCIES

Even under the best of conditions, things can go wrong. Last winter, when it was 40 below, I took off with full throttle out of a village on the Kuskokwim. As soon as I got aloft, I tried to throttle back but the cables were frozen in place. There I was at 1,000 feet with a full throttle and no way to turn it down. What did I do? I knew what the problem was, so I began climbing. When it's $-40\,°F$ on the ground, it's probably a lot warmer up top. As soon as I gained enough altitude the temperature went up, the cabin warmed up, and the frozen cables thawed. Then I regained control of the aircraft. Low temperatures will slow down your control freedom, so plan on it and adjust for it.

It's also important to mention that there is no good reason for anyone to be flying around when it's $-40\,°F$ on the ground with no inversion. If it's $-40\,°F$ on the ground and $0\,°F$ or better 1,000 feet off the ground, that's different. But if you have a cold snap that takes the temperatures of the atmosphere down that low, even the seasoned bush pilots don't go up. It's too risky.

It's also important to note that cold weather does more than just affect your engine. It affects the metal as well. Rivets shrink and the skin of the airplane becomes loose. The fuselage itself will shrink. Metal fatigue is enhanced and what would have been serviceable at $10\,°F$ or $15\,°F$ is weak enough to shatter at $-40\,°F$.

Just as important as shrinkage is expansion. Different parts of the plane will expand in warmer temperatures at different rates. I took off from Lime Village when it was $-40\,°F$ on the ground. But by the time I got to 3,000 feet it was $30\,°F$. There was a $70°$ difference between the ground and high altitude air temperatures. On the ground, everything had shrunk because of the cold. But when I was at 3,000 feet, the paint on my plane expanded faster than the fuselage. By the time I landed in Anchorage, I had lost almost all the paint from my plane. It had expanded and blown off because the paint had grown faster than the metal.

Landing in extremely cold weather can be a problem as well. Your tires can split in two without you knowing it. Or you can hit the brakes and find that your rims have stopped rotating but that your tires are continuing to spin on the rims. Some pilots who do quite a bit of cold weather flying, drill screws through their rims into the tires (FIG. 3-15). This links the tire with the rim and keeps the tires from freewheeling, so to speak, when the plane lands. (If you replace your tires during the winter, be sure to replace your screws as well.)

48

Brian Nelson

Fig. 3-15. *When cold-weather flying, it is a good idea to over-inflate your tires or to run self-tapping screws through the rims into the bead of the tire. This is to preclude the rotation of the tires when you step on the brakes in cold weather.*

Another method of keeping your tires secure to the rims is to double the air pressure and inflate the tires until they are round. It's also a good idea to paint a mark across the tires and the rim. Then, throughout the winter, you can check to see if the tires are moving on the rims. Three months later if you see that the mark on the tire is not in line with that on the rim, it's time to put in more air—and make another paint mark.

Be sure to leak the excess air when the temperature goes up!

One quick note on braking in cold weather, resist the temptation of excessive brake usage. Don't stomp on the brakes. Not only will you wear out your brakes faster than normal, but you will put yourself at risk. The brakes could lock. And don't use your parking brake while you are stationary for extended periods of time. You could find that it has frozen in place.

Another tip I've picked up over the years is to lock your plane. Quite a few pilots don't. For some reason they feel that if someone wants to steal something they'll be able to get into the plane anyway. That's true. But what I worry about are the kids that find an open plane and get inside. They may not steal anything but they might leave the door open. Then I get snow inside the plane and an open door that will slam around in the wind, maybe even act as a sail. Locking your door will avoid that problem.

Even when the weather warms up there are problems. The ice can be a foot or more thick and it is still possible to have a film of water on the ice. This can happen any time during the winter but will usually happen in the spring just before breakup. If you try to land on the ice, you could find yourself hydroplaning. Your wheels aren't actually on the ice, they are on a film of water and you do not have firm control of your direction of travel. Sideslipping is possible and your could find yourself spinning out of control (FIG. 3-16).

Fig. 3-16. *Water on the landing strip can cause hydroplaning even if the landing strip is unpaved. Good pilots avoid landing where they must plow through standing pools of water. Not only will the water cause loss of control of the aircraft, the pool might hide a pothole.*

Wet, heavy snow will also be a problem. It will slow you down quickly on your landings but makes takeoffs difficult. Many pilots run into trouble when they think they can power their way through the wet snow to get the airspeed they need to take off. Sometimes this doesn't work. They put on the power and move forward faster and faster and then run out of distance. What they should have done is pack down the landing area first.

When it comes to landing in cold weather, particularly on ice, keep in mind that temperatures vary from place to place, even from day to day in the same location. Ice thickness is not consistent from one area to the next. For safety, require at least a foot of ice on which to land or take off. While it is not possible to test ice thickness while you are in the air, look for signs of weakness before setting down. Are there cracks in the ice? Do you see any inlets where the ice might be thinner than expected? If you can, do a touch-and-go and then look at the tracks in the ice. Do they fill with water? If they do, fly elsewhere. If you don't see any water, try a second pass, make a slide for 200 or 300 yards to reveal the snow depth.

When you touch down, do not land in the sense that you cut power and allow the plane to come to a stop. Sweep around the area where you have landed in a "Figure 8" pattern. Ice is not of uniform thickness. By performing the Figure 8 you will be able to assess the landing and takeoff suitability of the ice over a wide area. This will be your takeoff strip, so make sure it is solid. Very solid.

Once you've made the decision to land, do not stop until you are exactly where you want to be. Don't land on the ice and then maneuver to your destination. Whenever I land on ice, I try to put the plane as close to shore as possible. If the weather gets warmer and the ice begins to erode, I want to be on the shore if any trouble develops.

Warmer temperatures bring other problems. If the temperature goes up to around freezing, you could have freezing rain. If you can't land, you'd better rise. Get out of that freezing rain and into warmer temperatures as soon as possible. While this is logical, the problem many pilots have is that they are caught in a situation where they cannot land and they cannot rise either.

I was flying an aircraft equipped with tires under a cloud bank over Cook Inlet when I hit freezing rain. I couldn't land. If I rose into the clouds, I would have been forced to fly blind and there were civilian and military planes in the area. But since I had no choice, I rose into the clouds and kept my heading. As the ice on the wings melted, I went below the clouds again and flew VFR until the ice built up on the wings again, forcing me to climb higher. I hopscotched across 100 miles of water that way and I'm here to tell the tale. It might have been a totally different story had I been in mountainous terrain.

Over the years I've heard a lot of people make all kinds of claims about icing (FIGS. 3-17 and 3-18). One of the most common claims is that you can spray your wings with PAM, the vegetable based, nonstick cooking spray. I've even known people who use it. While I'm not saying it won't work, I would say that to depend on it is foolhardy. Tricks to avoid icing can give you confidence where none is warranted (FIG. 3-19).

Since the subject of confidence has come up, it's important to keep in mind that the number one cause of accidents is human error. About 90 percent of all accidents are caused by human error. As a pilot you can significantly reduce your factor of error by thinking ahead. Flying may be fun but it is still work.

The chief cause of aircraft accidents in Merrill Pass, for instance, is not flying high enough. Pilots fly into the pass at 2,000 feet, even though the highest point of the pass is 3,000 feet. They're flying level and watching the ground come up, that is,

Fig. 3-17. *Icing on a plane can add hundreds of pounds in a matter of minutes.*

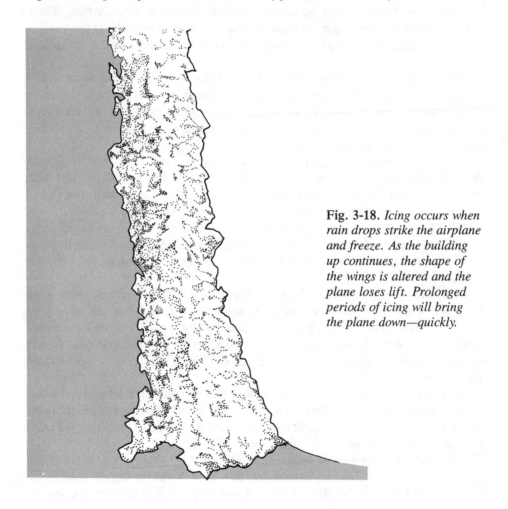

Fig. 3-18. *Icing occurs when rain drops strike the airplane and freeze. As the building up continues, the shape of the wings is altered and the plane loses lift. Prolonged periods of icing will bring the plane down—quickly.*

Fig. 3-19. *Dramatic landscapes make flying a pleasure, winter or summer.*

increase in altitude. They think they are gradually climbing but, in reality, they are flying level and the ground is coming up. Suddenly they find that they need to climb another 1,000 feet and they don't have the time or distance to do it safely.

Now they have a grim choice. They can try to turn around or fly forward. The situation is exactly the same on an aborted takeoff. You barely get up off the ground and your engine quits. What do you do, fly forward and look for a place to land or turn the plane around?

Unfortunately that's a tough question. In my experience, those who have gone forward have lived a lot more frequently than those who have tried to turn the plane around. The biggest problem with turning is that you will run out of altitude before you can complete the maneuver. You start your sweep and you make your turn but you don't have any altitude.

The best way to solve this problem is not to get yourself in that situation in the first place. If you know that the highest point in Merrill Pass is 3,300 feet, then fly above 3,300 feet as you enter the area. Fly smart, stay alive. If you think ahead, you will prepare ahead (FIG. 3-20).

I would also like to add another note of caution. Don't assume anything when you are flying. In the Merrill Pass area, some pilots decided to avoid the Pass area by flying at 5,000 feet, quite a bit higher than the highest point on the pass. They took off

Fig. 3-20. *One of the greatest joys of flying safely is the opportunity to travel where you otherwise could not go by road or even foot.*

from Anchorage and headed east. If the weather is clear, this is not a bad idea. If the weather is overcast, it's a whole different story. Flying at 5,000 feet often puts you into the clouds. The results of flying blind and trusting to the compass can be seen on the upper slopes of Mt. Spurr. Right now there are two planes that are buried up to their tails after having hit the mountain head-on in the cloud cover. They could not have done a better job if they had tried to do it on purpose.

When it comes to flying—and particularly winter flying—I follow the rule that I do not have to go up but I do have to come down. I do not have to make any trip, but once in the air, I will have to come down. You always have a choice. Even under the most severe of conditions, you have a choice.

My personal rule is that if I choose to fly, I must have at least three options. If I don't have those three options, I do not fly. If I am flying with a twin otter with floats and one engine goes out, I have the option of flying on one engine or landing on the water. Thus I have three options: fly on two engines, fly on one engine, or land on the water.

Fine, you say, suppose you are flying over land, what would your three options be then? In that case, I would fly higher. If both engines went out, I would have the altitude to glide to water. If my route took me over an area where this was not reasonable, I would not fly. Period. If I do not have three options for staying alive, I do not go. That rule has kept me alive for over 14,000 flight hours in Alaska (FIG. 3-21).

Fig. 3-21. *Glacier flying is spectacular but be aware of possible dangers. Depth of field may be impaired and the sun's light, bouncing off the ice flow, can reduce visibility.*

4
Mountain Flying

THERE IS AN OLD ALASKAN BUSH TALE, POSSIBLY TRUE BECAUSE THE pilots do not laugh, of the sourdough who bought a plane that was so old it didn't have any instruments. Rather than fork out the money for an altimeter, artificial horizon, and directional gyro, he just got a compass, a cat, and a duck. The compass told him which way to fly. As he flew through clouds, he kept his eye on the cat that was on the seat beside him. Since a cat will always sit with its head level, if the cat dipped its head to the right, the sourdough pulled the right wing tip up until the cat's head was level.

For the altimeter, he used the duck. If he could not see the landing strip clearly, as he came down he kept a sharp eye on the duck. As soon as the plane was about to reach ground level, the duck would suddenly become active and start flapping its wings to cushion its own landing. Then the sourdough knew that terra firma was imminent.

While this story is a shade beyond the edge of believability, when the authors mentioned this to a grizzled bush pilot, his reaction was "Why didn't he use a spark plug?" When asked to explain, the old-timer stated that the pilot in question could have dispensed with the cat by simply suspending a spark plug from the top of the windshield. By keeping an eye on how the spark plug hung, the pilot could have avoided the leans. "Saves on mice too," he remarked.

While these home-spun flying tips are great for a book, it is not recommended for any pilot, no matter how grizzled. But, giving credit where credit is due, it is interesting to note that the legendary Wiley Post used to hang a heavy steel ball from the ceil-

Fig. 4-1. *Long shadows with low sunlight make mountain flying a pleasure.*

ing of his cockpit. However, the reader should not jump to a conclusion. Post felt that if he fell asleep on a long flight and the plane went into a dive, the ball would slam into his head and wake him up. It is logical to suppose that Post's invention of the automatic pilot was motivated at least in part by his desire to reduce the number of lumps on his head.

In a more serious vein, mountain flying can be one of the most exhilarating experiences of your life (FIGS. 4-1, 4-2, and 4-3). It can also be one of the most frightening. Unlike flying in parts of the United States where there is room to land—and then some—if you have trouble in the mountains in Alaska, it will be hard to find a smooth, flat area on which to set the plane down (FIG. 4-4).

Before mountain flying is even discussed, it is critical to note that the single most important aspect of mountain flying is the simplest: file a flight plan. No one expects to go down, it just happens. Then it's too late to file a flight plan. Unfortunately, every year there is someone who does not follow this basic of basics and disappears. After searching a wide area, the person, or wreckage, is found in an area where no one would have expected the plane to have been. Having a flight plan means that you will be picked up soon. Not having a flight plan means that you get to spend a few days in the bush sitting by your radio with crossed fingers and a signal mirror. Be intelligent. Don't let a clerical error compound your human error.

Fig. 4-2. *Mountain flying doesn't just mean flying in the mountains. There are many high altitude meadows where the intrepid pilot can land to ski, hunt, or winter camp.*

59

Fig. 4-3. *Often, bush pilots navigate up streams and rivers. They pay close attention to cable crossings, which are usually marked with several red balls attached to the wires.*

Brian Nelson

Fig. 4-4. *During the winter, many airstrips are not maintained. Before you use the strip, do a flyby to ascertain its condition before you land.*

When it comes to mountain flying, one of the worst problems to be faced with is turbulence. Winds rushing over mountain crests cause downdrafts and turbulence, turning a pleasant flight into a battle with the elements. While turbulence can sometimes be predicted, in most cases pilots learn that prevailing weather patterns cause turbulence in certain areas. But if you are new to the area, you may be flying into turbulence without knowing it.

The best rule of thumb is to maintain as high an altitude as possible when crossing mountain ranges. Since mountain peaks divide weather systems as well as watersheds, be prepared for a change in both weather and turbulence. Flying high will give you the ability to minimize some of the discomfort.

To understand the effect of turbulence, think of the mountains as rocks and the wind as a 30-mile-an-hour stream. Where the stream rushes over those rocks there is a lot of turbulence. This is known as *mechanical turbulence* (FIGS. 4-5 and 4-6). On one side of the rocks there is a powerful upwelling and, on the other side, there are downwellings, as well as a great variety of unpredictable cross currents. A plane flying from one weather system into another over a range of mountains would have the same problems as a small fish trying to get over those rocks without being battered to death on the rocks.

Another problem that will complicate flying in the conditions above is known as a *mountain wave*. This occurs when there is a strong wind that hits an immovable

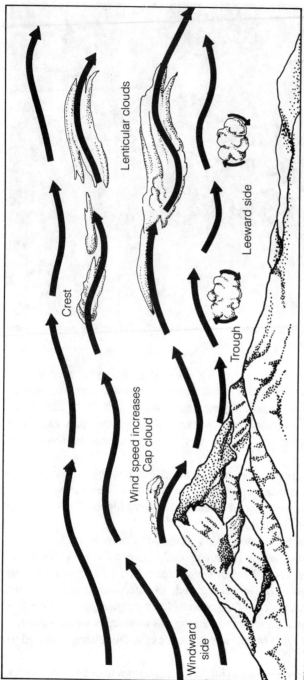

Fig. 4-5. *Airflow over a mountain.*

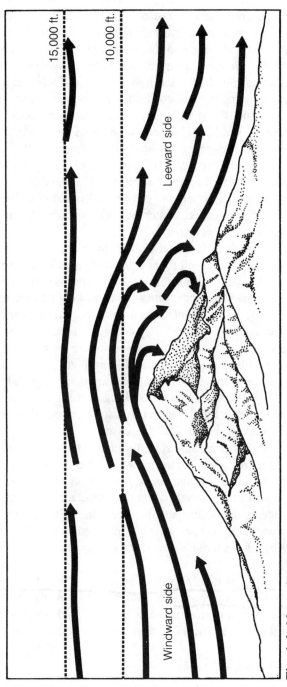

15,000 ft.

10,000 ft.

Leeward side

Windward side

Fig. 4-6. *Mountain wave.*

object, a mountain for instance, and the air mass is forced up, over the mountain, and then into the next valley. If the air blankets on the far side are unstable, the more stable air mass will nose into the ground and bounce. Rebounding, the wind will hit the unstable air mass from below and be driven by its own force down again only to bounce again. Under the right conditions, this bouncing can go on for hundreds of miles. Flying in these conditions will be uncomfortable, to say the least.

A pilot flying up a canyon will also have trouble with mechanical turbulence. If there is a wind blowing across the top of the canyon, the pilot might not know it until he or she rises above the level of the canyon wall. If there is any indication at all, it will be in the form of a wind that appears to be blowing down one canyon wall and crossing the flight path. The pilot will learn of the severity of the winds only when he or she actually crests the canyon and is removed from the protection of the canyon walls. You can effect a smoother ride by staying low in the canyon. Just make sure that the canyon is not boxed.

Then there is the possibility that winds are blowing right up a canyon. Because the canyon walls will funnel the wind, it will increase in speed. This is known as the *venturi effect*. This mechanical turbulence is particularly powerful in mountain passes where wind from one watershed is blasting into the next.

Judging mountain drafts is based as much on personal experience as on your ability to read the weather. If you fly in the same area for a long period of time, you become used to the idiosyncrasies of the terrain. One of the clues you will probably use will be weather systems. Flying high over a mountain range you will have the opportunity to see what weather conditions you will be facing. If it is clear where you are but you can see clouds spilling over the top of a mountain range in the direction you intend to travel, be prepared for some rough weather. You're going to be treated like a tennis shoe in a clothes dryer.

To be on the safe side, fly high. Many pilots err by not gaining enough altitude before crossing a mountain range. They approach the range at a lower altitude and plan to climb over the peaks. This, however, can lead to problems if the climb does not start early enough. Then the mountains rise faster than expected and the pilot is suddenly out of time and distance. He can't make the turn to escape and he can't fly forward. Or he rises where he planned to spiral upwards and finds that mechanical turbulence is buffeting his plane so brutally that he is in danger of losing control (FIG. 4-7).

Perhaps the first rule of mountain flying is to never fly lower than the highest point on your route. This will give you plenty of clearance and you won't have to worry about running into a mountain. It's also a good idea to stay out of clouds. Many of them have "rocks" in them—and those rocks are called mountains.

FLYING MALADIES

Climbing high, however, can lead to other problems. If you are planning on flying above 5,000 feet, learn the warning signs of *hypoxia* (a condition in which less oxygen

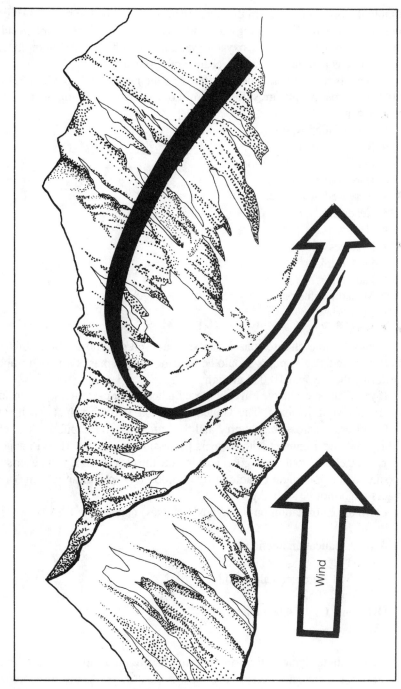

Fig. 4-7. *The path of flight for a limited-area or box-canyon turn.*

Wind

gets into the bloodstream from the lungs than is needed by the body). Oxygen starvation is a better way of explaining the condition. Since the air is thinner at higher altitudes, obviously there is less oxygen available. The higher the pilot flies, the less oxygen there is and the greater the chance of hypoxia.

While it is rare for someone to suffer from the ravages of hypoxia at 5,000 feet, by 15,000 feet most people are suffering from one of its many symptoms:

- Loss of night vision.
- Blurred vision.
- Loss of peripheral vision.
- Unexplained anxiety.
- Increased heart rate.
- Headache.
- Nausea.
- Dizziness.
- Slow thinking.
- Fatigue.
- Mental confusion.
- Euphoria.

A pilot could even lose consciousness as a result of hypoxia. Since this is a condition that is predictable, pilots should be wearing oxygen masks for flights above 5,000 feet during the day and 10,000 at night.

If you plan on extensive travel at these higher altitudes, you might consider taking special classes on hypoxia. The United States Air Force conducts such classes at a number of bases across the country and they are open to the public. The classes are held in a safe environment with hypoxia professionals present. If you intend to transport passengers, it would be a good idea to take the class even if you never suffer from hypoxia. While you might be able to fly at 6,000 feet comfortably, some of your passengers might not be so lucky.

For more information on the hypoxia classes, contact the FAA or write to:

Airman Education Section
AAM-142
FAA Civil Aeromedical Institute
P.O. Box 25082
Oklahoma City, Oklahoma
73125

High altitude flying will also result in pressure build-up in the ears and sinuses. As you rise, the ambient pressure decreases with altitude. As the air becomes thinner, pressure is lessened. Each of us has the physical ability to adjust the pressure within our ears. On the ground, our ears adjust to the pressure gradient. As we fly, our ears are required to adjust to the new pressure. As you take off, your eardrums extend out in the sense that the pressure inside the ear is greater than that outside and your eardrums bubble out as a result. The human body, however, adjusts for this change by allowing air to escape through the eustachian tube, which connects the ear with the throat. The bubble of the eardrum disappears. Thus the ears have adjusted for the new ambient pressure. When you level off at 5,000 feet, your ears will stabilize as well.

Conversely, as you begin to descend, your body adjusts for the increase in air pressure. Since your ears are adjusted to 5,000 feet, when you descend there is more pressure outside the ear than inside. This causes a slight concavity of the eardrum. The body adjusts for this imbalance by allowing air to rush back up the eustachian tube and to increase the pressure on the inside of the eardrum. Thus the ears will "pop" as the pressure equalizes.

If your ears do not clear automatically, much of the pressure can be relieved by yawning or going through the motions of chewing gum. Rotating the jaw is also a common method of equalizing the air pressure in the ears. If none of these methods work, professionals recommend the *Vasalva maneuver*. In street terms, this means to hold your breath and your nose and blow gently. This will force air up your eustachian tubes and force your eardrums to clear out. Basically this means that the pressure on the *inside* of the ear is now equal to the pressure on the *outside* (FIG. 4-8).

Fig. 4-8. *These ear plugs are specifically designed to allow pressure to be released from the inner ear yet, at the same time, provide hearing protection from loud engine noises.*

It should go without saying that this maneuver is only good for rising in altitude, not falling. If you have difficulty clearing your ears on the way down, keep a small bottle of nose spray in the glove compartment.

There are a variety of pressure sicknesses of which the pilot should be aware. If a passenger or the pilot have been skin diving within 24 hours of flying, there is a chance that he/she might get a case of *aviation bends*. This is a variation of the decompression sickness suffered by skin and deep sea divers. Because a diver is breathing compressed air, an abnormal amount of nitrogen is absorbed into the bloodstream along with oxygen. The oxygen is used by the body, but the nitrogen remains in the blood. Having nitrogen in the blood is not dangerous as long as it is allowed to exit.

If the diver has been down a long time, he or she will have to decompress, that is, come up slowly enough that the nitrogen that went into the blood with the compressed air will be released slowly and escape from the bloodstream into the lungs. From there it is exhaled. If the diver comes up too fast, however, the reduced pressure will force the nitrogen to form bubbles in the bloodstream. These bubbles will clog in the joints, forcing the victim to bend over in excruciating pain; hence, the name of the disease.

Aviation bends is a variation of this diving disease. If a diver flies too high after an underwater excursion, the miniscule amount of nitrogen left in his system might begin to bubble. Like the deep sea bends, these nitrogen bubbles clog in the joints and cause a great amount of pain. Should this occur, it is advisable to seek a lower altitude immediately. Better yet, land and wait 24 hours before flying again, as you should have done in the first place.

Another high altitude ailment that a pilot might encounter is hyperventilation. This occurs when there is too much oxygen in the bloodstream. If you want to know what hyperventilation will do to you, stand calmly and take about 20 deep breaths in rapid succession. (Make sure there is a soft sofa behind you before trying this maneuver.) What you are doing is supersaturating your bloodstream with oxygen. As the oxygen level rises higher and higher, your body will cut off your ability to breathe. In other words, you will black out. Under the best circumstances, you will get dizzy and lightheaded.

Hyperventilation can occur in a stressful situation when a pilot is breathing too rapidly because of nervousness. The best way to avoid the effects of hyperventilation is to control your breathing. If you suspect that you are in danger of suffering from this ailment, slow down. Breathe less frequently. If this is a problem, breathe into a paper bag. This will increase the amount of carbon dioxide in your bloodstream while, at the same time, reduce the amount of oxygen. Since there are very few pilots who have paper bags sitting around in their cockpits, count on controlling hyperventilation by avoiding tight spots and, when in them, force yourself to breathe normally.

Another breathing danger is the intake of carbon monoxide. The body needs oxygen to survive; that's why we breathe. Unfortunately, your body likes carbon monoxide. In fact, your bloodstream is 200 times more likely to absorb carbon monoxide than oxygen. This means that, given the choice, your body will absorb carbon monoxide much, much faster than oxygen. If this happens over a long period of time, your body will suffer from oxygen starvation, and eventually you will die.

Carbon monoxide poisoning is *extremely* dangerous because you will black out before you know that you are in danger. This gas is colorless, tasteless, and odorless. It is a by-product of your plane's exhaust system and does its damage by infiltrating your cabin (FIG. 4-9).

On the upside, while it is impossible to smell the carbon monoxide itself, you *can* smell exhaust fumes. That's one of the unexpected fringe benefits of the internal combustion engine. If you happen to smell exhaust, that's a very good sign that carbon monoxide is building up in your bloodstream.

Fig. 4-9. *Be sure to check your exhaust frequently to avoid carbon monoxide poisoning.*

To avoid disaster, there are a number of actions you can take. First, spend a few dollars on a carbon monoxide detector. Second, make certain that all the seals on your exhaust system are new. If the seals are more than a year old, replace them even if they look brand new. Third, just on the off chance that there is a leak in your fire wall, crack your windows every once in a while to make sure that there isn't a carbon monoxide build-up.

However, just because you don't smell exhaust, this does not mean that there is no build-up of carbon monoxide in the cabin. As mentioned before, you will not know that there is a problem until you black out. Then it is too late to open a window.

Incidentally, should you suspect that you are being poisoned by gas, land as soon as possible. It will take at least a day for the carbon monoxide to dissipate from your blood system.

There is another category of flying maladies, known as *illusions*. "It's not what you do know that should concern you," the old saying goes, "It's what you believe to be true that just ain't so." An example of this flying condition is known as the *leans*. These usually occur when a pilot has to make a correction in the plane's attitude. When the maneuver is achieved, or at least so says the artificial horizon, the pilot has a feeling that the plane is not at the proper attitude. In spite of the fact that the instruments indicate that the aircraft is in proper stead, the pilot *feels* that the instruments are in error (FIG. 4-10).

Brian Nelson

Fig. 4-10. *Complete instrument panel.*

Trusting his sense rather than his instruments, the pilot adjusts the attitude of his plane to fit what his sense of balance tells him. This is usually very dangerous. In almost all cases, the instruments are a much better judge of your attitude than your ear canal. While it is certainly true that instruments, on occasion, can fail, in almost all cases you will be flying safe by trusting your artificial horizon, turn coordinator, airspeed indicator, and altimeter rather than your sense of what is correct.

A wide variety of illusions can affect a pilot, including:

- **spatial orientation**—a condition in which objects that cannot move appear to do so.

- **Coriolus illusion**—a condition in which it appears that the plane is rotating.

- **graveyard spin**—a condition, aptly named, in which the pilot rotates the plane to the right but feels that the plane is rotating to the left. The pilot then rotates the plane the way he feels it should be and goes into a downward spin.

- **inversion illusion**—a condition in which the pilot feels that he is leaning too far backwards during periods of rapid acceleration or takeoffs. Pilots suffering from this illusion will push their noses down, which could cause other problems.

- **elevator illusion**—a condition in which the pilot feels that he is gaining or losing altitude even though the instruments do not show it.

- **runway and terrain slope illusion**—a condition in which the pilot believes he is too high or too low on landing. In attempting to correct the descent, the pilot will overcompensate and place himself and his aircraft in danger.

- **false horizon**—a condition in which the pilot sees a horizon that is not there.

- **auto kinesis**—a condition in which lights will appear to move if the pilot stares at them for a number of minutes.

- **runway width illusion**—a condition brought on by a narrow runway that causes a pilot to feel that he is too high on landing.

- **featureless terrain illusion**—a condition that exists when there are no features on the terrain on which the pilot can focus his eyes. This would be like flying over miles and miles of ice sheet.

- **ground lighting**—a condition in which a pilot believes that car lights, street lights, or house lights are actually landing strip lights.

To fully understand the impact of illusion, see if you can find a copy of Escher's drawings in your library. Escher does optical illusion drawings such as water collecting in a pool formed by a waterfall and then flowing into a pool that feeds the original waterfall. While many readers have seen these drawings before, reexamine them, but this time, note the background. Because of the way Escher draws the background, the lines enhance the illusion. Parallel lines drawn at an angle, for instance, will make your mind automatically adjust to make them level. This then lets the artist fool your senses.

But Escher's drawings are just drawings, you say. What do they have to do with flying? Take the runway and terrain slope illusion from the list above. If you concentrate on an object without taking into account the characteristics of the background, you could become the victim of an illusion. Your eyes can play tricks on you, not because of what they actually record but because of what you think you see.

HORSE SENSE

When it comes to mountain flying, Doug Geeting of Talkeetna has had his share of experiences. With more than 14,000 flying hours, he is recognized as one of America's foremost mountain pilots. No stranger to mountain flying, Geeting flies mountain climbers and scientists onto Mt. McKinley, the highest mountain in North America. Geeting is the first to know, as he states it, that "horse sense is more important than horsepower."

The most important piece of equipment on your plane rests between your ears. The plane is just a collection of metal, wire, glass, fabric, and solder. *It* doesn't fly; *you* fly. You as the pilot are responsible for everything that you can check. Trust your instruments; but double-check them. If the gas tank gauge says full, check it. If it says empty; believe it (FIG. 4-11). If you expect to be flying on extended range tanks, check them too (FIG. 4-12).

Fig. 4-11. *If your gas gauge says empty; believe it.*

Fig. 4-12. *A belly tank offers the pilot extended range for long flights.*

Part of that responsibility is to stay attentive. Complacency will kill you. Don't view flying as simply a pleasurable activity. It's a serious responsibility. But then again, it's *your* life that's at risk (FIG. 4-13).

Fig. 4-13. *Winter flying often means getting into areas that were unreachable during the summer.*

5
Takeoff
and Landing Tips

YOU DON'T HAVE TO GO UP BUT YOU DO HAVE TO COME DOWN. THERE'S A lot of truth to that statement. Actually the tough part is not coming down; it's coming down when and where you want (FIG. 5-1).

Under normal conditions on normal runways, neither takeoffs nor landings are difficult. Unfortunately, there are not that many normal runways in Alaska. Alaskan pilots don't know what normal conditions are. They are so used to conditions being in flux that they expect the unexpected.

Perhaps the most important rule to keep in mind with regard to bush takeoffs and landings is that you have to choose where to land on the basis of where you want to take off from.

While this seems fairly obvious, many pilots don't think of landing in those terms. They take off for a fly-in fishing trip, land on a remote lake, and spend the day drowning worms. Then, when they want to take off, they find that the wind is blowing from the mountain side of the lake and there are rocks that cut their takeoff strip in half. Worse, the only area that is left has a river entrance that makes the waters turbulent about one-third of the way into the takeoff and, at the far end of the lake, is the highest stand of trees in North America. Sure, they could corkscrew the plane up off the water on the so-called "small lake takeoff," but it's been quite a few years since they've tried that and now there's a crosswind.

This is a disaster in the making. But it could have been avoided. Since the pilot had been looking for "just any old place" to go fishing, any other place would have been just as good as this one. If he had been thinking about taking off while he was

Fig. 5-1. *Sheer mountainsides make landing treacherous in an emergency.*

looking for a landing area, he would have spotted the rocks, the tall trees at the end of the best takeoff area, and the river inlet. If the wind had been blowing when he landed, he might have even been able to detect the direction of the blow by looking at the telltale bending of tree branches. The best advice to the pilot in the spot above was not to have gotten into it in the first place.

Think about where you can take off from *before* you land. That's just common sense. You can touch down in a lot fewer feet than you need to take off, particularly if you've got a moose on board. That is, if you have a dead moose on board. If you have a live moose on board, you deserve all the trouble you get.

Landings and takeoffs are also affected by elevation and atmospheric conditions. Because air is thicker at lower altitudes, the blanket of air on the runway at sea level is thicker than on a landing strip at 1,000 feet. As a result, takeoffs at sea level can be steeper. If you leave from Anchorage, which is almost sea level, and fly up into the Chugach or Alaska range, you're going to need more feet to land than if you were returning to Merrill Field in Anchorage.

Secondly, because heat causes air to expand on a hot day, the air is less dense than on a cold day. This, in turn, means that your takeoff from Merrill Field on a cold day will allow for a steeper climb than on a warm day (FIG. 5-2).

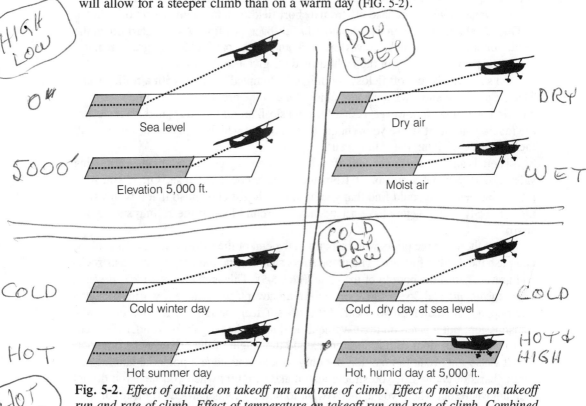

Fig. 5-2. *Effect of altitude on takeoff run and rate of climb. Effect of moisture on takeoff run and rate of climb. Effect of temperature on takeoff run and rate of climb. Combined effects of altitude, temperature, and moisture on takeoff run and rate of climb.*

Combined, the altitude and atmospheric conditions will affect your takeoffs and landings tremendously. If you take off from Merrill Field on a cold morning and only use a few hundred feet of runway, don't expect to be airborne in the same distance when you take off from a gravel strip at 1,000 feet in the Alaska Range at three in the afternoon on a hot day. Conditions have changed; adjust for them.

Wind is also an important factor. If possible, you should plan to take off and land into it.

If there is a crosswind, many pilots want to *crab* (FIGS. 5-3 and 5-3A). This does not mean to get down on all fours and move sideways, although the direction of travel is similar. To correct for a crosswind, you angle, or crab, the plane into the wind. This technique works well on descending, but you must straighten the path of the plane before you hit the runway.

Short-field landings and takeoffs are always exciting (FIG. 5-4). Because you don't have the distance for a smooth, graduated incline or decline, you have to eyeball where you want your wheels to touch down. Your angle of approach will be significantly steeper, and once you have arrived at the beginning of the landing area you will have to drop your nose and land quickly. You must be at minimum controllable airspeed when you hit the ground. If not, you might hit the other end of a short landing area.

Conversely, when you take off from a short field, you are going to get one shot at it. One. That's it. Taxi with the elevators in full-back position. As you start down the field, you may have to rock the wheels back and forth, particularly in grass or mud. When the plane is pointed in the right direction, give it full power.

On short fields, or soft fields, you might be tempted to begin with a rolling start. That's fine if you know what you are doing. One of the problems with rolling starts on any kind of a runway, however, is that fuel can slosh around in your tanks. If it sloshes too much, you might starve your engine for a moment which, in essence, removes all the advantage of doing the rolling start.

There is also the matter of centrifugal force. Landing gear is not made for moving sideways. If you put strain on it from the side, it could collapse. Or, if you have retractable gear, you could find that you have bent it just enough so that it won't slide into the belly. Taildraggers have a tendency to ground loop if the rolling start is too sharp.

Then there are the pilots who back up to the end of the runway, lock their brakes, and push the throttle forward. The plane starts shaking and the prop wash blasts rocks and gravel against the bottom of the plane (FIG. 5-5). This is not a good idea. It wears down the engine and doesn't give enough of an advantage to make it worthwhile. It's like popping the clutch on your car. All it does is tear the living daylights out of the transmission, put a patch on the pavement, and make the neighbors wonder if a teenager is living next door. But it does not extend the length of the driveway by one foot.

It's also important to note that not only should you judge a potential landing site on the basis of taking off, you should also make sure that when you land you do not stop anywhere but where you actually want to park. This is particularly true for both water and ice landings. If something goes wrong, you have to be positioned to take

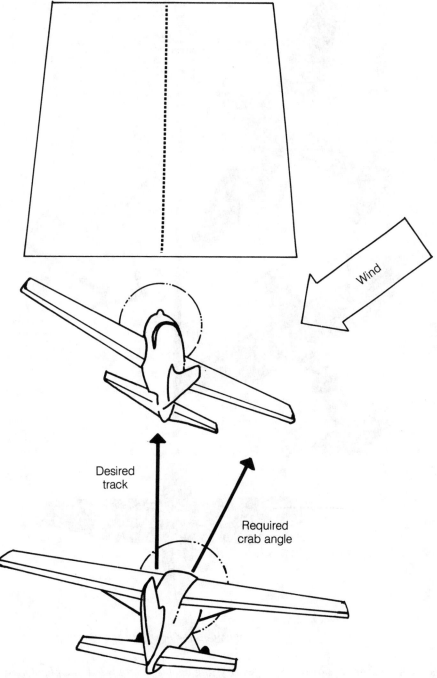

Fig. 5-3. *When there is a wind blowing across the runway, it will be necessary to crab when making your final approach.*

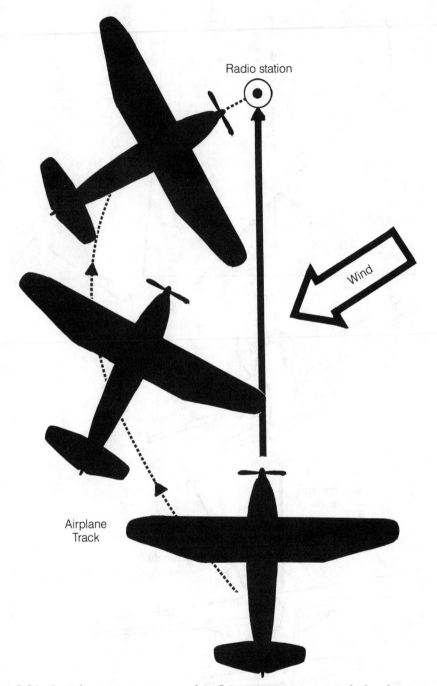

Fig. 5-3A. *In order to stay on course when flying against a crosswind, the plane must be crabbed into the wind.*

Fig. 5-4. *Having a "short runway" means taking into account hazards such as boats that might pull into your path. For water landings, keep in mind that there are day-to-day changes in the obstacles at the end of your landing pattern. Take these changes into account before you land.*

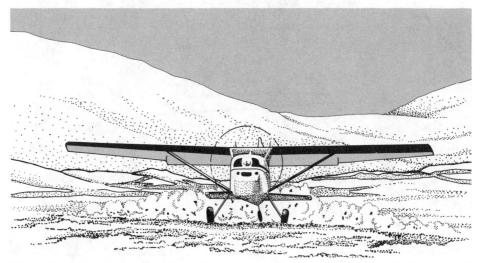

Fig. 5-5. *When landing or taking off from a gravel runway, a plane may kick up gravel, sand, or small stones.*

care of yourself and see that a minimum of damage occurs to the plane. If you land on the ice and it turns out to be too thin, you want to discover the bad news when your plane is on the shore, not in the center of the lake (FIGS. 5-6, 5-7, and 5-8).

Fig. 5-6. *Not all landing strips are the same from day to day. Note the mud and water on this strip that might not have been there the day before. Take into consideration the time of the season as well as the time of day when choosing your landing site.*

Anchorage Museum of History and Art

Fig. 5-7. *A PBY lands on Marsden matting in the Aleutian Islands despite the mud.*

Brian Nelson

Fig. 5-8. *Using a city street as a taxiway is a common practice in many rural areas. Watch out for pedestrians and cars and be sure to use your landing lights to warn off traffic.*

LANDING GEAR

Quite obviously, landing gear is an important part of your plane. If you are planning to do most of your takeoffs and landings from a paved strip, then a tricycle gear will do just fine. On the other hand, if you are planning on doing bush flying, you might be better off with a taildragger. It has a more rugged landing gear, is easier to fit with skis and, because of its construction, its propeller is mounted higher, making it less likely to pick up and throw back stones and gravel from rough landing strips.

Fixed landing gear is also recommended over retracting gear, which is great for pavement and other surfaces that are consistently good from one end to the other or from one season to the next. Bush flying requires being prepared for any condition of landing strip *except* consistency from one end to the other and from season to season. The fixed gear is also dependable when the gear is ice-coated: it stays down (FIG. 5-9). Retractable gear cannot make the same claim. On snowy fields, the gear can become clogged with snow. Then, when it's retracted, the snow freezes and, in turn, so does the gear.

Fig. 5-9. *Pressure ridges can be very dangerous when taking off or landing.*

For warm weather flying, or for flying in temperatures as warm as they get in Alaska, stick to tires and floats—just make sure you use the tires for the land and floats for the water. Large, or tundra, tires (FIG. 5-10) are great but are not always needed. Regular tires are fine in most cases, but if you want to upgrade, look to a 650 × 6 or 850 × 6.

Twenty-nine-inch tires are a little much, but there are some bush pilots who swear by them. Their added width gives the plane the ability to roll over debris that otherwise might have been tossed up and back by the propeller. Small holes in the runway aren't a problem with large tires either.

Brian Nelson

Fig. 5-10. *Tundra tires.*

On the other hand, large tires are not an asset on macadam landings. They grab on the asphalt and, in a taildragger, that means the plane might nose forward. If you put too much brake on the plane, or you have extended-range fuel tanks that further lean the plane forward, it is possible to stand the taildragger on its nose when you land with tundra tires on a cement or macadam surface. Large tires are also heavier than conventional ones and therefore reduce cruise speed.

SHORT TAKEOFF AND LANDING KITS

Quite a few Alaskan pilots also swear by *STOL*, short takeoff and landing kits. Engine upgrades and, of course, the addition of air scoops on the wing tips can allow a plane to take off and land on shorter fields. But think twice before adding STOL equipment to your plane in order to take advantage of shorter runways (FIG. 5-11). If you have to depend on equipment rather than flying ability to utilize certain strips, you are asking for a disaster. Takeoffs and landings can be tricky and STOL is not going to give you a significant advantage, at least not for the amount of money you'll have to spend to shave a few feet off your landings and takeoffs.

Fig. 5-11. *A modified STOL aircraft. Note the drooped wing tips and larger engine. The leading edge or "cuff" of the wing on this plane is moveable to give more lift area to the plane.*

On the other hand, depending on the weight and model of your plane, you can save yourself about 40 percent of your landing field with STOL. The drooped wing tips, aileron flap interconnections and gap seals, and leading edge slats will increase the surface areas that give you lift, and the engine and propeller modification will give

Fig. 5-12. *A popular wheel/ski arrangement.*

Perhaps your greatest problem when it comes to landing on snow or ice is that from the air the surface appears featureless. Even when the long shadows of evening come, the landing area can look pancake flat when, in actuality, it has quite a few terrain aberrations.

Before you land, look for visual reference points such as where tree trunks disappear into the snow. Are there rocks visible above the snow level? You can also drop something that will show up against the surface of the snow, such as a thick, bright red ribbon tied around a piece of firewood or a black garbage bag weighted with a can of soup. Anything on the ground you can use to give you a visual reference is advisable.

If you are planning on flying all winter, be aware of the fact that ice rots. As temperatures climb, the ice sheets on lakes become honeycombed. From the air the ice may look solid, but if you land on it, it may very well collapse. If you have to fly in the transitional weeks between solid ice and clear lakes, stick to pontoons and land in the ice leads, the open water area between the lily pads of ice (FIG. 5-13).

Water takeoffs and landings are a shade different from those done on land. First of all, eyeballing the landing area is critical. Even if you have landed in the same spot for years, check it out. The Alaska bush is famous for its changing character. Rivers rise and fall, sand bars appear and disappear with irregularity, logs and branches float in, and surface scum appears.

As an interesting aside, the Exxon Valdez oil spill in 1989 taught Alaska's bush pilots a few new lessons about landing on featureless surfaces. When oil covers the water, it acts as both a reflectant and a shroud. Where the oil was thick, it would not ripple. This caused concern among pilots because it was hard to judge where the surface of the water actually was. Even near small inlets and outlets, where a pilot could expect to detect *riffling*, which is slight, erratic movement, there was none.

Another problem was with shrouding of the waters. The oil was often thick enough that pilots could not see what was lurking just below the surface. Experience has shown pilots that the lapping action of the waters will reveal the location of rocks and logs that lie partially submerged (FIG. 5-14). However, since oil shrouds the water, it is impossible to see rocks and logs even if they were near the surface.

For water landings use normal power on with full flaps (FIG. 5-15). Once the floats touch the water and the plane starts to settle, increase back pressure to full up elevator, and hold it while reducing power. River landings should be done in the same way, the major difference being that the water on which you are landing is moving rapidly. If you have a favorite spot for landing and taking off on the water, you might think about anchoring an empty plastic bottle a little more than halfway down your usual landing strip. This will serve as your go-no-go indicator.

If you don't feel you have enough room for a safe water takeoff, you might consider a small lake takeoff. This is a technique where you fly around the lake. Plan your circle so that you will be able to take off into the wind. In a small lake takeoff you should add power on the turn and step up much earlier than if it were a normal, straight takeoff from a long lake. Be sure not to apply full power until you are actually facing the direction in which you wish to take off.

Fig. 5-13. *An amphibious float offers the opportunity to land on water or land.*

Fig. 5-14. *Be aware of tidal changes that allow rocks to "appear" and "disappear" as the water falls and rises.*

Fig. 5-15. *Once a floatplane is "on step," it can easily lift off the water.*

Landing on unconventional runway strips is the riskiest venture of all. An unconventional runway strip is a stretch of ground or frozen water that someone spots and says, "Hey, we can land there!" Be wary of people who say that and of the stretch of hard surface they seem willing to let you land on.

Landing on a gravel strip requires a bit more experience than macadam or cement do. There can be potholes filled with water that you cannot see or branches that are so perfectly camouflaged that you will not see them until it is too late (FIG. 5-16). Loose stones and gravel are also a problem.

Fig. 5-16. *Potholes on a paved strip, a danger to all aircraft.*

92

The best advice for landing on gravel, as on ice, is to plan for a long landing. Stay off the brakes as long as possible. Once you touch the brakes, you will probably get a spray of gravel that will pelt the underside of your aircraft and wings. This is not good for the paint job. It is also not a good idea to get rocks into your flap crevices. Once you have stopped, it would be a good idea to check for debris.

If you are planning on landing on a beach you have never walked, choose your strip carefully. If the tide is out, look to land between the high and low tide marks. This will assure you that you are landing on the firmest possible ground. If the tide is in, see if you can land near the high tide mark, even if there is a bit of water on the sand or gravel.

Watching the waves break and run up the beach, you should be able to judge the depth of the water at the high tide mark. But be careful. While landing in a thin sheen of water may make a great photo, it's got some problems associated with it as well. First, you cannot actually see the surface, so you don't know if there are any potholes. Second, bouncing water can hide large rocks, which are hell on landing gear.

Third, if you choose your angle wrong, you could find yourself bouncing off the BLOCK + TACKLE hard sand and into the soft stuff. This means you had better have a shovel and winch and be prepared for some heavy work. It could be even worse if you bounce the wrong way and end up in shallow water in a rising tide with a broken landing gear. In this case, you should have your swimsuit along as well.

Beached icebergs are also a problem. While they can usually be spotted from the air, when they get small they look like stones. Worse yet, if they were very large before they shrunk, they might have left a crater that is now filled with dark water. These craters look just like land, but if the wheel of your plane drops into a hole left by one of these ice cakes, you could be in for a long wait on the beach.

It would be foolish to assume that a pilot is smart enough to pull his or her plane above the high tide mark. Just in case you think otherwise, don't. Once you have landed, make sure your plane is moored above the high water mark. Even if you plan to be gone for just five minutes, get your plane above the high tide mark.

The most spectacular takeoffs and landings are vertical. These are also the most dangerous. Even if you are an expert pilot with thousands of hours, you should be extremely cautious when attempting a vertical takeoff.

Vertical takeoffs and landings can only be done in high winds. The usual procedure—not that there is anything usual about a vertical takeoffs and landings—is to head into the wind, extend flaps, and settle down slowly. If the wind stays strong enough, the plane will settle.

But you have to be extremely careful. I once pulled a climber off a mountain with a vertical landing. He was in a tent when he heard me coming. I settled into a vertical landing and the wheel hit the tent. One second the tent was there, the next it was gone, like a magician had poofed it into thin air. That climber was in bad shape; he had no choice but to get off the mountain. It was fly with me or die of hypothermia. I must

have hovered for about two or three minutes while he climbed aboard. Once I saw both his knees, we were gone. By the time he shut the door we were away. But a landing and takeoff like this is only for an expert. If you're reading this book, you're not an expert yet (FIG. 5-17).

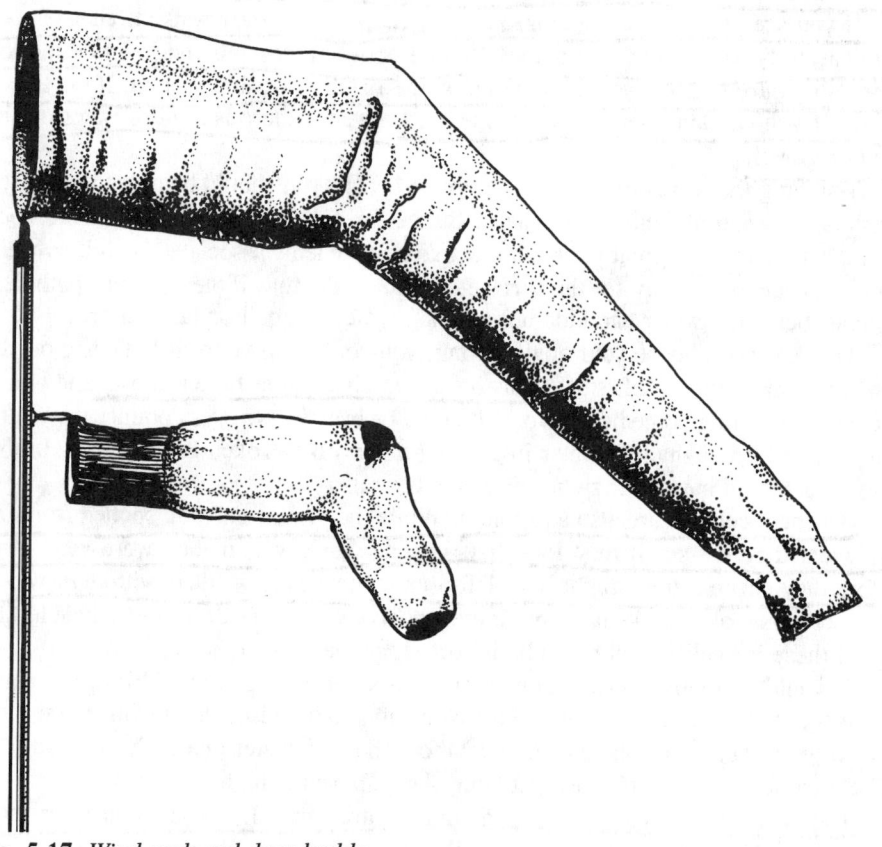

Fig. 5-17. *Wind sock and darn buddy.*

6
Navigation

ONE OF JIMMY STEWART'S GREAT MOMENTS ON THE SILVER SCREEN CAME when, as a young Charles Lindbergh in *The Spirit of St. Louis*, he searched the heavens for the Big Dipper so he could complete his epic flight from New York to Paris. While the scene is pure Hollywood, it does underscore the problem that pilots have always had. Once you get up, how do you know where you are?

THE EARLY DAYS OF AVIATION NAVIGATION

Aviation has come a long way since the early days when direction-finding meant carrying a compass and a star chart in your breast pocket. In the early days of aviation navigation, maps were unheard of. Most pilots flew in the areas with which they were familiar. If they needed to venture out of their own turf, they talked with other pilots who were familiar with that terrain. There were maps, of course, but nothing like the topographic sections and orthophotoquads we have today.

But it didn't take long for the pilots to realize that they needed some kind of ground markers from which they could orient. Even if they knew the area well, cloud cover and/or darkness could blanket the land. The first on-the-ground directional beacons, so to speak, were bonfires. Still used today under emergency circumstances, bonfires are lit to display a runway, usually in a field. Easily identifiable against the blackness of night, a pilot can steer for the runway and land safely.

The bonfire technique, however, proved woefully inadequate. While it was a sterling aviation guide if the night was dark and clear and the plane was in the area, other-

wise, it was an all-night chore keeping the fire lit as well as an all-day chore gathering the firewood for the next night. Worse, on rainy days the bonfire might send up more smoke than fire if the wood burned at all.

By the mid-1920s, another system of navigation was instituted. Across the United States, a network of light beacons and emergency landing fields were established; thus, a pilot could take off from one city and follow the lights to his destination. The emergency landing strips were for the pilot who was in trouble and on course. It was a great idea for the time and by the end of the decade there were about 10,000 miles of network in the United States.

Unfortunately, there were some drawbacks to the system. First, of course, 10,000 miles—when considering all the landing strips in the United States—isn't much of a network. Second, the lights were hard to see during the day and only really usable on clear nights. While the beacon system did enhance aviation safety somewhat, it did so at a high cost.

The next step was to use the radio. In the heyday of the light beacon network, experiments with a radio beacon network began. This proved more effective than the light beacon system and became the rage. Though there are few of the old radio range stations left, at one time they were state-of-the-art.

VHF OMNIDIRECTIONAL RANGE (VOR)

Today we use a far more sophisticated system, the VHF omnidirectional range, known as *VOR* (FIG. 6-1). VOR stations were just coming on line when World War II struck, so it was not until the 1950s that VOR station building boomed, and it was not until 1971 that a nationwide network was completed. Today the network includes about 950 stations coast to coast.

Basically, a VOR is a station that emits an electronic pulse that can be interpreted into 360 directional beams called *radials*. A VOR detector in the plane receives the electronic pulse and the pilot chooses a radial in the direction he wishes to travel. The

Fig. 6-1. *VOR-LOC, CDI with compass.*

VOR detector then interprets the timing sequence, finds the correct radial, and follows the beam toward or away from the VOR station.

While there are many forms of directional navigation, the VOR is the most popular. Not only is it relatively easy to use, the equipment is not very expensive. Further, with the wide variety of radials available, the pilot has 360 degrees of choice. VOR frequencies are virtually free from static or interference caused by storms or other weather conditions and are accurate to within a degree or two. For bush pilots in particular, the VOR is a blessing because it allows a pilot to navigate directly down a beam without regard to the wind drift. The VOR also takes into account the change in magnetic north, a factor Alaskan pilots rely upon since the farther one flies north, the more magnetic north varies.

To make the VOR as easy as possible to use, each station is listed on aeronautical charts. Shown in blue surrounded by an *azimuth symbol* (a circle with degrees marked off), the format of the listing makes it easy to use the VOR's information with the assistance of a straightedge and pencil alone. That's quite a jump from the days of flying from bonfire to bonfire. The VOR station's name is listed within the azimuth, as well as its frequency, station code letters, and Morse code identification.

The Morse code identification is important because it serves to identify the VOR station. This is particularly important in areas where two or more VOR stations radials converge. Voice transmission can identify the VOR, of course, but the Morse code provides an excellent backup, particularly with regard to unmanned stations. These unmanned stations are also known as *slave stations* and are operated remotely by a master station.

The manned VOR stations broadcast weather conditions at 15 minutes past the hour. You should be able to pick up those weather forecasts if you are within 150 miles of the VOR station.

Inside the plane, the VOR indicator has three different components to assist the pilot in navigation. The first is the *CDI*, or course deviation indicator. Also known as the *left-right needle*, the CDI appears as a needle in a gauge pointing at a crescent with two sides. Once the CDI has locked onto a VOR radial, the needle will indicate if the plane is on course. As long as the needle stays at the apex of the crescent, the plane is on course with the radial. As the needle begins to swing, the pilot knows he is slipping off course.

The second gauge of importance is the *TO-FROM Indicator*. This instrument, of course, lets the pilot choose whether he is following the radial *toward* the VOR station or *away* from it. It is important to note that the CDI will only tell you if you are on course. It will not tell you which direction you are traveling. This gauge is actually a switch and appears as a white arrow indication TO or FROM.

The third gauge on the VOR indicator is the *course selector*. Usually this appears as a compass with a flagged needle indicating direction of travel. The course is shown at the top of the dial.

Operating a VOR is quite simple. As the plane approaches a VOR station, tune the VOR indicator to the frequency printed on the navigation charts. The station will be

identified by a Morse code beep of the letters of the station. The beeping will continue every five seconds around the clock. Turn the volume on your radio up to identify the station by its Morse code and then turn your volume down after you have confirmed that you are on course. If you can't read Morse code, wait until 15 minutes after the hour when the VOR station will broadcast its identity and the latest weather report for its area. Once you have identified the VOR station, set the course selector to the desired radial. Once you have locked on to the radial, be guided by your CDI, the left-right needle.

As great an advance as the VOR is, it is not without its difficulties. The first is that since VOR is a radio signal, it is a line-of-sight mechanism. As long as there is an unobstructed track between the VOR station and the plane, the VOR will work efficiently. However, if the plane drops to an altitude where a mountain range blocks the signal, the VOR will show no signal (FIG. 6-2).

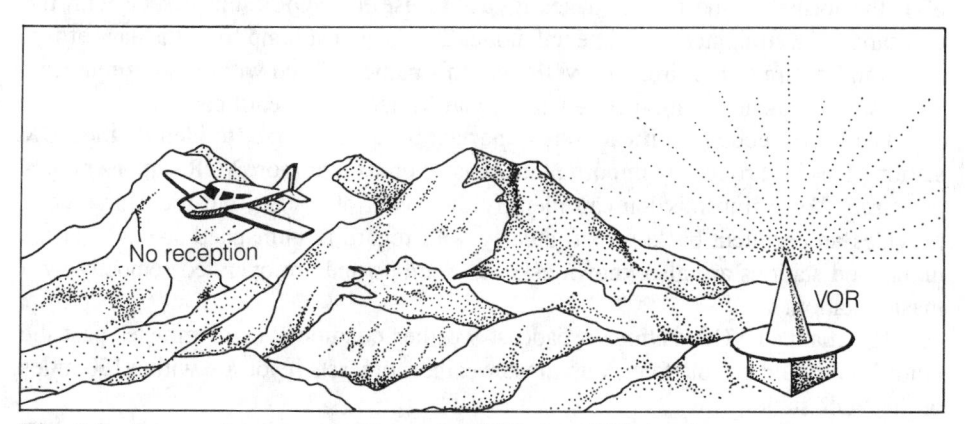

Fig. 6-2. *A mountain or mountain range will block a VOR signal.*

Second, there is the question of accuracy. The usual procedure for a pilot using VOR is to station-hop across the country. As each radial takes the plane within range of the next VOR station, the pilot switches radials. However, the farther a plane is from the VOR station, the greater is the linear discrepancy. In solid numbers, if a plane is 60 miles from the VOR station, the radial is one mile wide. What this means to the pilot is that he is not following a tiny stream of electrons. What he is actually navigating along the farther he gets from the VOR station is an ever-widening pathway. If a pilot is navigating over long distances by VOR in places like Alaska where the stations are widely scattered, it's a good idea to keep this linear discrepancy in mind.

DISTANCE MEASURING EQUIPMENT (DME)

Another piece of equipment commonly found in bush planes is *DME*, distance measuring equipment (FIG. 6-3). Basically an airborne radar, the DME transmits a

Fig. 6-3. *DME (distance measuring equipment).*

signal that is automatically returned by a ground station. Measuring the time that it takes for the signal to return, the DME gauge will indicate in nautical miles to the VOR station.

Using the altimeter, VOR, and DME, a pilot can accurately describe his position to an air traffic controller. However, it is important to note that the slant range, that is, the nautical miles from the plane to the VOR station, is affected by altitude. The higher the plane is flying, naturally, the farther it is from the VOR station.

AUTOMATIC DIRECTION FINDER (ADF)

Another navigation instrument found in many bush aircraft is the *ADF*, the Automatic Direction Finder (FIG. 6-4). The ADF has a frequency selector that allows the pilot to lock onto a low/medium frequency station and then home to its signals. In other words, if the pilot has no VOR, he can use the ADF to identify and navigate toward a station.

Fig. 6-4. *ADF (automatic direction finder).*

TRANSPONDER

While not many bush planes have *transponders*, federal regulations now require all planes flying in controlled airspace to have them aboard (FIG. 6-5). A transponder is essentially a black box that plugs into the altimeter through an altitude encoder and issues a specific identifying number. With the transponder, air traffic controllers can identify aircraft and make specific recommendations to them over the air. Without the transponder, the controllers can only tell from their radar that a plane is within the range of their equipment. Unfortunately, they do not know the altitude or speed of that aircraft.

Fig. 6-5. *Transponder.*

LONG RANGE AID TO NAVIGATION (LORAN)

A very expensive piece of equipment that most bush planes do not have is a *LORAN*, Long Range Aid to Navigation (FIG. 6-6). LORAN was originally set up as a marine navigation system rather than as an aviation system.

To provide an accurate means for ships to navigate over tossing ocean waves, the United States Coast Guard established a network of LORAN stations around the world. Set in patterns of threes, a ship could pick up the three signals and triangulate its spot on the map.

While LORAN is incredibly accurate, there is a downside, and that is cost. Even though the black boxes are getting cheaper, they are still more expensive than many pilots can afford. Further, when the LORAN gives a position, it is in latitude and longitude, which is useful only if you have a map handy on which you can pinpoint your position.

OTHER NAVIGATION AIDS

One of the most important pieces of navigational equipment is a *wet compass*. This is best described as a floating compass in a transparent case that is secured to the top of the instrument panel. As the plane turns, the compass case turns but the compass panel remains in place (FIG. 6-7).

Fig. 6-6. *LORAN.*

Fig. 6-7. *Gyrocompass.*

Finally, don't forget that the most reliable pieces of navigational equipment are maps. You should always fly with maps and a hand-held compass, just in case. Even if you are absolutely, positively sure you know where you are, don't take it for granted that your instruments are correct. Why not? Consider this: On December 22, 1989, a Thai Airlines 747 was picked up by an Anchorage air traffic controller heading east due south of St. Paul on St. Lawrence Island. The controller called the airliner and the pilot stated he was headed west on a flight from Seattle to Tokyo. "WRONG!," said the traffic controller. The Thai Airlines was 600 miles off course and flying on a course that was 180 degrees different from what his instruments told him.

Don't be stupid; carry maps and a compass (FIGS. 6-8 and 6-9).

Fig. 6-8. *Be sure to set the LORAN before you leave the ground. You want to include where you are and where you want to go. This particular setting is for a trip from Anchorage to Barrow.*

Fig. 6-9. *Always remember to set the altimeter to current barometric pressure before taking off.*

Brian Nelson

7
Emergencies and Thinking Ahead

EVERY BOOK ON FLYING—OR CAMPING FOR THAT MATTER—HAS A SECTION on survival. It's an important chapter, of course, but the advice is the same and roundly ignored by almost everyone who reads it. In fact, the only people who read chapters on survival and take the advice to heart are those who have had a brush with the crueler side of the great outdoors.

Unfortunately, about 90 percent of the people who go into the wilderness, whether they fly, walk, or boat, are totally unprepared to survive longer than 24 hours after they are due back. For survival gear, they carry some extra matches, a Rambo knife they bought for $19.95 filled with cheap, useless geegaws, two feet of twine, and a signal mirror with Morse code engraved on the back.

Surviving is a noble enterprise, the stuff of best-seller books. But it is not so noble while you're doing it. You had better do it right the first time; you won't get a second chance.

When it comes to survival, the most important decisions you will make happen long before you get in the plane. Far too often pilots simply throw together a survival kit based on a hypothetical list in some book. They lock the kit away in a compartment and never give it a second thought. Worse, they follow the state law to the letter and only carry those items that are required. What they are actually doing is packing the absolute minimum and expecting it to save their lives. In Alaska, only 11 items are required by law:

1. Food for each person for two weeks.
2. An axe or hatchet.

3. First aid kit.
4. Firearm and ammunition.
5. Gill net or assortment of fishing line and gear.
6. Knife.
7. Two boxes of matches.
8. Mosquito head net for each person on board.
9. Two signaling devices.
10. One pair of snowshoes per person—required during the winter only.
11. One blanket for each person over 4 years of age. (FIG. 7-1).

Fig. 7-1. *Small, compact survival kit.*

This is certainly a fine list. It is a fine list to help you survive if your floatplane's engine won't start and you are marooned on a lake next to a stream during June when the salmon are running and there is plenty of dry firewood on the shore and you can radio for help but have to rough it for 24 hours waiting for the weather to lift. It would certainly be nice if every accident happened under these conditions. Unfortunately, that's not the case.

The first decision you make, and ultimately the one that could mean more to saving your life than any survival kit, is how you dress when you step into the plane. The most expensive survival kit on the market will do you no good at all if it is locked away in a compartment in a plane that is sitting at the bottom of a lake.

Your first rule of survival is to dress as if the plane were going to go down. If it's winter, make sure you are dressed for winter travel on foot. Concentrate on layers of clothing. The layers trap air between them, which your body warms, creating layers of insulation. Wool is an excellent insulator even if it is wet; cotton saturates very quickly and once wet is useless as an insulator.

Take a pocket of your parka that can be zipped closed and put in a selection of gear such as waterproof matches, a fuel block, three or four plastic garbage bags, a smoke signaling device, and a pocket knife. *CANDLE*

To increase your margin of safety, buy one of the many pocket-sized survival kits on the market. As an added bit of advice, don't take a manufacturer's word as to what is actually in the kit. Investigate it yourself. Then and only then zip it into your parka pocket. If you can't find these at a local sporting goods store, check the advertising section of flying or camping magazines. Northern Cross Ltd. (Route One, Big Springs, Kansas 66050) sells two small survival kits, the smaller about the size of a fat Magic Marker. Survival Supply Company (P.O. Box 972, Camino, California 95709) also produces survival kits—and has some excellent fuel bars. Lake & Air, Inc. (in Eden Prairie, Minnesota, 55344) and Safesport (in Denver, 80211) both have complete survival kits.

The second rule of survival is to expect the unexpected. While the chance of your plane going down is slim, don't assume that when it does you will be prepared. No one expects to crash, but if it happens, you must be prepared to survive under the most brutal conditions imaginable. As you fly, play the "What If" game. This could mean the difference between life and death.

You play the "What If" game by imagining the worst possible circumstance and then working through it. For instance, you might say yourself, "What if the plane hits a tree unexpectedly and is thrown to the ground? I have a broken leg, cannot reach the survival kit, and the radio is out. What do I do?"

Gruesome though this circumstance is, the question to be answered is, "Can I survive?" A possible answer might be, "If it was during the winter, I would use pieces of the airplane to build a shelter or windbreak. I would put a handful of snow into one of the plastic garbage bags in my pocket and put it inside my parka. When it melted, I would have water. I would use a fuel block, which I have in my pocket, for heat and signal search planes with a smoke device, which I also have in my pocket. I could use pieces of the broken landing gear along with the seat belts and wiring to bind my broken leg. I would expect a search party to fly in from the south because I filed a complete flight plan, so I would have to make sure that my signal was visible from that direction."

As you tick off the possible problems, visualize the possible solutions. Do you have everything you need in your pockets? If not, why not?

You should also have a survival manual handy—and particularly in the plane. A Boy Scout or Girl Scout handbook is adequate, but just barely. These books are written for healthy, athletic youngsters who are lost for a few days during the summer. While there is no best survival manual, two worth buying are *The Armed Forces Sur-*

vival Manual (Rawson, Wade Publishers, Inc., New York) and Gene Fear's *Surviving the Unexpected Wilderness Emergency*. Fear's book, incidentally, is published by the Survival Education Association, 9035 Golden Given Road, Tacoma, Washington, 98445.

There are two other books that are worthy of at least a glance. Mel Tappan's *Tappan on Survival* (Janus Publishers, 1981) has an excellent section titled "Survival Library." Tappan's book concentrates on urban survivalism but it does have some interesting tidbits for wilderness survival. Another urban survivalist book is *Tom Brown's Field Guide to City and Urban Survival* by Thomas Brown, Jr. and Brandt Morgan (Berkeley Books, 1984). What makes *Tom Brown's Field Guide to City and Urban Survival* notable is the variety of uses he illustrates for common household items. Why is this a significant survival manual for the bush pilot? Because you might find yourself stranded in an area where there are cabins and some of those common items may be present. For a specific example, many bush residents live in their cabins only part of the year. To eliminate fire hazards, they might take the wires off their generator. Had you read *Tom Brown's Field Guide to City and Urban Survival*, you would know how to hook that generator up. That knowledge, in itself, would be worth 10 times the price of the book.

If you are going to travel over water, a good book is Dougal Robertson's *Sea Survival; a Manual* (Praeger Publishers, Inc., 111 Fourth Avenue, New York, New York, 10003). Robertson's book includes some tips on survival that even the experienced wilderness hand could use, such as innovative fish traps and solar stills to transform salt water to fresh—or polluted swamp water to drinking water.

THE EXTRAS

In the event of a crash, your chances of surviving are increased significantly if you have prepared your plane for that eventuality. Just as in a car, your seat belt could save your life. How old are the seat belts in your plane? Have you ever replaced them? Have you checked their housing lately? Do you have shoulder straps? When did you check them last? If you answered these questions by saying that you have never replaced the seat belts or straps and the last time you looked at their housing was 10 years ago, you have an immediate chore to perform. If you have to crash land, you can expect some G forces. If you jerk to a stop after 3 seconds at 60 knots, you can expect a force equivalent to 2 G. You can survive this if you are strapped in properly.

WINTER

If you are flying during the winter, make sure you load sleeping mats and sleeping bags. Once on the ground, your biggest problem will be combating hypothermia. You can conserve your body heat best by staying in a sleeping bag, but you cannot stay warm in a sleeping bag unless there is some insulation between it and the ground. Newspapers, seat cushions, or aircraft carpeting work well.

You will also be better off if you can build some kind of shelter. If the plane cabin is still functional, use it, but do not start a fire there; you could end up, quite literally, burning yourself out of house and home. If you are going to buy a tent for survival purposes, make sure you buy one that has an external frame. They are quite a bit easier to erect and don't need stakes to stay erect.

If your plane is white, you should have some brightly colored material on board—royal blue is best against white snow. Keep in mind the *Rule of Contrast*. Search parties are going to be looking for something that is out of the ordinary: an orange plane against white snow, for instance. If there is a chance that your plane would be mistaken for the background, do something to make you or the plane visible. Drag out anything that has a different color than the ground. Light three fires in a row. If it is night and you cannot start a fire, use a flashlight to snap out signals. Put up a flag using your red long johns. Don't rely solely on your ELT.

SUMMER

CARRY WINTER WING COVERS RED OR FLOORSENT SIGNALS, SHELTER, SLEEPING BAG.

Survival on the ground during the summer is as much a battle to stay dry as it is to stay warm. You should also be prepared for rain. Since most people do not carry rain gear, put some large plastic garbage bags in your survival kit. If it rains, rip a hole in the bottom of one of the bags for your head and a hole in each side for your arms. It may not be the best rain jacket in the world but it will work well enough.

At the risk of a few hoots, you might want to throw some condoms into your survival kit. No, they are not for use in those unexpected encounters on the trail. Rather, they can be used to carry water or, if there is damage to your fingertips, the condoms can be pulled over bandages, allowing you full freedom of your fingers while protecting your wound at the same time.

In the summer, as in the winter, remember the Rule of Contrast. The rescue party will be looking for something different on the ground. Give them something to spot. During the summer, with the wide variety of colors on the ground and, in many places, the lack of open meadowland, you will have to be clever. Bright red or yellow work well as long as you choose your background correctly. Signal fires are good and so is "SOS" written in some visible form.

FIRE

Once you are on the ground, your first responsibility is to the injured. Unless the plane is on fire, teetering on the edge of an abyss, or about to be devoured by Rodan, *don't move any victim*. Since most rescues happen within 24 hours, the victim is better off remaining where he or she is for that time. Moving could damage the person worse than they already are, particularly if they have a back injury—which is quite likely in a plane crash.

Once the injured have been taken care of, your next job is to start a fire. This is important for a variety of reasons, even in summer. First, it attracts attention. Second,

it provides a source of warmth as well as a means of cooking the food you have in your survival supplies. If you have to stay on the ground for a day or two, you are going to need the fire to purify your water. Perhaps just as important, if your survival kit doesn't contain insect repellent, you are going to need the smoke screen to keep the bugs away.

While matches are obviously the method of choice to start a fire, you should have included an option in your survival kit. Flint and steel are easy to include in a survival kit, while a cigarette lighter is small enough to be dropped into your pocket. Mirrors from the plane can be used, as can lenses from a camera or pair of binoculars. Rubbing two sticks together can produce fire if you know what you are doing—but there are a lot of Boy Scouts who cannot make fire this way—and you can even use your airplane's battery to start a blaze. To use the battery, arc a spark through oily rags. *Be very careful when using gasoline to start a fire.*

Some people even make their own fire starters. To make a fire starter, find an old shotgun shell—empty, of course—some kitchen matches, and a candle. Light the candle and melt wax over the heads of the kitchen matches, one at a time. Place the matches inside the shotgun shell and cover the opening with wax. If you put the matches head down, you can pop open the shotgun shell and use them one at a time. If you put the matches head up, you can ignite them all at the same time and they will blaze together. This method is particularly useful when lighting a fire with damp wood. The matches in the shotgun shell will burn like a candle, long enough to dry the wood and then set it ablaze. For best results, make sure you get wax inside the shotgun shell. The more wax there is, the longer your "candle" will burn.

Another trick involves Vaseline, a plastic camera film container, and a cotton ball. Fill the film container about one-third full of Vaseline and jam the cotton ball inside. The cotton will act as a wick and the Vaseline as the fuel. Once lit, the concoction will act as a candle. As long as the airtight cover to the film container is in place, the volatile oils will not evaporate.

When your fire is not being used to cook or purify water, toss on some green branches or rubber from the aircraft. Put up a cloud of smoke and give your rescuers something to look for. Remember that three fires in a row is the signal for distress.

FOOD

When it comes to food, trust to your survival kit. Most rescues come within a few hours after you are reported missing, so you are better off staying near the aircraft. Don't wander off and become lost.

If it appears that rescue is not going to come before your food runs out, or you have gone down on your way to a hunting area and are not expected back soon, you should start hunting right away. In this case, use your survival pack food for an emergency.

In most cases, your best bet is small game. Rabbits, squirrels, groundhogs, and

110

birds are abundant and can be snared. If you didn't bring snare wires, use some of the wiring from the plane. Some seat covers have cord in them as well. Use smaller diameter wire.

When setting up your snares, look for game trails. Broad, well-traveled trails mean moose. Because you won't be in a position to snare a moose, your best snaring will be on trails that show signs of small animal passage. Loop one end of the wire around a bent sapling or tie it to a large rock. Then, make a trigger so that when the wire is pulled, the sapling snaps or the rock falls. Set four or five along the trail and then leave the area for a dozen hours.

If you prefer to hunt rather than snare, make yourself a spear or a bow with a set of arrows. Use the extra blade in your Rambo knife for the spear point. If you happen to be in the market for a survival knife, make certain that there is an extra blade hidden in the scabbard. You can use that blade to make—or be—a spear point or to carve sharp points on arrows. Some of the knives come with the makings of a slingshot as well. If you are going to spend the money, go first class. Make sure your knife has a compass, a waterproof compartment for matches, an extra blade, and slingshot setup.

When it comes to larger game, you can use the firearm and ammunition in your survival kit. A .22 is good for most game. If you have packed nothing but *bear insurance* (in Alaskan jargon, that's a .357 Magnum), you could be in trouble. A .357 won't leave much of a rabbit and isn't large enough to kill a grizzly bear unless you are a very, very good shot. If you are in bear country, be careful about killing large game close to the wreck. Once you've brought your moose down, you could find that a bear is as interested in the moose as you are. Unfortunately, you will not be able to leave the area, and a bear in the vicinity of your campsite can make the most seasoned of sourdoughs nervous.

For this very reason, many pilots mount gun cases on the outside of their planes (FIG. 7-2). Primarily for convenience's sake, it is also a good backup if and when you need a heavy firearm.

If you haven't made your choice of firearms yet, you might consider a 12-gauge shotgun. This will give you a wide variety of load, from bird shot to slug. An overunder is a good, but expensive choice. A survival .22 is also an excellent choice because of its light weight, durability, and ability to be broken down and packed inside its own stock. It weighs about three pounds plus the weight of the ammunition. The .22, however, is a good survival weapon in your pack, but not necessarily on an airplane.

What can you eat? A better question is what *can't* you eat. With a few exceptions, you can safely eat anything you can catch. Toads are not good for eating; if you don't know the difference between a frog and a toad, don't eat either one. Clams may not be good, depending on the season, and bear is edible as long as you really cook it. Bears can have parasites, like trichinosis, which can infect a human body. Bears are also dangerous to eat because, should you wound rather than kill one, you might find yourself in the uncomfortable position of wondering who is going to eat whom.

111

Fig. 7-2. *Some pilots store their guns on a gun rack outside the plane.*

WATER

Water is a real problem. While you can put off eating for a few days if need be, you cannot do the same with drinking water. The average body needs about 2 gallons of water a day, every day. Dehydration can occur anywhere, desert or snow-covered meadows, and even if you find a source of water it may not be drinkable.

The simplest way to make water drinkable is to boil it. While the alternatives include purification tablets or mixing iodine in the water, overall your best bet is to boil it.

AIRPLANE TOOLS AND GEAR

Just as important as what goes into your survival kit is what is in your plane that can be used when you are on the ground (FIG. 7-3). Next time you take inventory, make certain that you have a strong flashlight with extra batteries onboard. A fire extinguisher is a must as well as an *ELT* (emergency locator transmitter) (FIG. 7-4). Look to see if the ELT turns itself on automatically on impact or must be turned on by hand. That would be something to remember in case of a crash.

Fig. 7-3. *Mechanic's repair kit.*

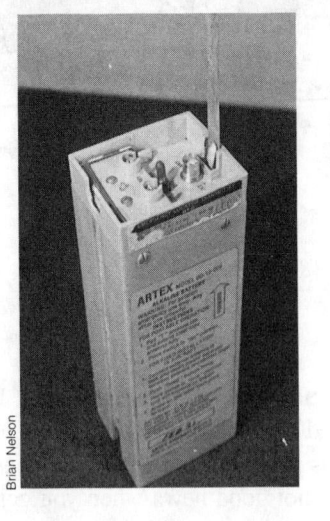

Fig. 7-4. *ELT.*

You should also make certain that there are both a Phillips and a regular screwdriver readily available as well as a crescent wrench, a pair of pliers, and a pair of wire cutters. You will need all of these to take apart sections of the plane to make a shelter on the ground.

A COMPREHENSIVE SURVIVAL KIT

There is no such thing as a complete survival kit (FIG. 7-5); however, a list of items that should be included is in TABLE 7-1.

In the long run, hope that the time, effort, and money you spend on the survival kit is a waste of all three. If you ever need it, you will find that every dollar you spend on being prepared increased your chances of survival substantially.

Fig. 7-5. *Large survival kit.*

MAPS

An excellent survival tool is a map. Unfortunately, depending on where you live in the United States, the information on which the map was based could be very old. While this is not bad news if you are considering the location of rivers and mountain ranges, it is not good news when you consider the location of cabins listed on topographical maps.

Because they are very light, buy yourself a set of topographical maps for those areas you frequently fly over. Aviation maps are great if you are flying, but topographic maps can't be beat when you are on the ground.

114

Table 7-1.

Essential

MAYBE —
Food and water for each person on board for two weeks
Hatchet or axe
First aid kit
Firearm and ammunition
Fishing supplies: line, hooks, sinkers, flies
NO — Rambo knife
Several boxes of matches
Mosquito head netting for each person on board
Two signaling devices
Snowshoes
Blanket for each person on board

(handwritten, circled) INFO FROM 1992
(handwritten) 15 YEARS OLD

Optional (Recommended)

BETTER CHOSES BIGGER BETTER — Flashlight with extra batteries	Condoms — NO
— Garbage bags	Tin cups
— Shotgun shell matches	Spoons
Insect repellent	Sun glasses
Compass	Survival rifle
Pocket lighter	Flint ——— BETTER
Snare wires	Cooking utensils
Billypot	Water purifier
GOOD — Ziplock bags	Screwdrivers
VISGRIPS — Pliers	Wrenches
ELT	Fire extinguisher
100 feet of rope	100 feet of twine
First aid kit	Space blanket — SPACE BAG
— Fuel blocks	Hard candy — NO
Small saw or cable saw	Shovel —
BETTER — Newspaper (to start fire)	Survival Manual
BETTER — Store-bought survival kit	Handheld ELT

TRANSPONDERS

One of the best pieces of survival gear, though it is expensive, is a transponder (FIG. 7-6). Costing about $3,000, this piece of equipment will squawk your location to air traffic controllers. If you buy the Mode C and hook it up to your altimeter, it will also indicate your altitude. While many pilots are not interested in spending that kind of money, particularly for older planes, it appears that requiring a transponder is in the future of aviation. If you fly in controlled airspace, transponders will probably be required within a short period of time—if they are not required now.

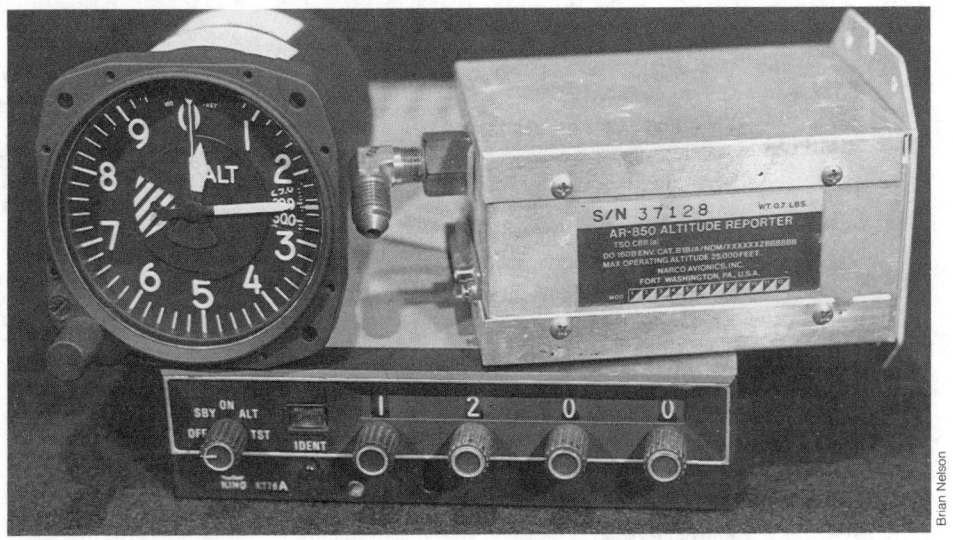

Fig. 7-6. *Altitude reporter system required for entering controlled airspace.*

EMERGENCY LOCATOR TRANSMITTERS (ELTS)

Perhaps the last thing most pilots think about is their *emergency locator transmitter* (ELT). That is, it is the last thing they think about until they need it. Then they get real concerned as to whether it works or not.

If you have an ELT—and you'd better because it's the law—and have not checked your batteries lately, put this book down, zip out to the plane, and eyeball the expiration date on the batteries. If you can't find the date, get rid of the batteries.

ELTs usually come with magnesium or alkaline batteries. The magnesium ones are good for three years, while the alkalines last two years. The general rule of thumb is to replace your batteries at 50 percent of their expected life. In other words, if the batteries are supposed to be good for three years, change them at a year and a half. If you leave them in place longer than that, they will probably be weak. Weak batteries are fine for a flashlight you use occasionally but not for an ELT on which your life may depend.

Be sure to check your ELT frequently. You should only check it during the first five minutes and the last five minutes of every hour. As long as you stay within this 10 minute band, no one will confuse the testing of an ELT with one that is operating because of an accident. Keep in mind that people make mistakes. After you have checked your ELT, make sure you *turn it off*! Don't be the cause of a false alarm. Worse, if you forget to turn your ELT off, you will extinguish the life of your batteries in three days and then your ELT will not work at all. That's a real risky proposition, even for a Sunday flier.

If you are buying an ELT, there are more than a dozen models on the market—complete with replaceable battery packs. One of the best ones on the market is the

ELT 910, and it costs a shade under $400. If you have had an ELT for a long time, you might consider getting a new one for another reason. There have been so many false signals that the new ELTs now have a narrower band of transmission. This means that there will be fewer false alarms. If you keep your old ELT, it means that if you have an emergency, rescuers might think your ELT is a false alarm.

If you are putting it into your plane, remember that the ELT works on forward G force. This means that it must be placed in such a manner that if the plane stops suddenly the ELT will be triggered. Don't put it in backwards. And don't dodge the FAA regulations by not putting one in at all. That's stupid, not to mention very dangerous.

Under ideal conditions, the ELT will operate for 72 hours. Its signal will be picked up on 121.5 MHz as well as by satellite. If you happen to be flying and pick up an ELT transmission, the first thing you should do—before you use your radio to call anyone—is make sure your ELT is turned off. Don't embarrass yourself by reporting an ELT distress signal only to discover that you are reporting yourself!

Additionally, if you have the money you should buy a handheld ELT. They only run about $100 and are not very heavy. If there is an accident, that handheld ELT will give you an extra margin of safety. It will also be critical to your survival if you decide that you have to walk out of the area. For the cost and weight, it's certainly worth your time.

WING COVERS

If you are thinking of buying wing covers, make sure you get some that are red or fluorescent (FIG. 7-7). They will add a margin of safety for you if you happen to go down. Light and serviceable, you can throw yours into the back of your plane with no appreciable loss of space, and if you need some visual markers for planes overhead, you can't beat them for their cost and weight.

FIELD REPAIRS

Perhaps the most difficult section in any flying book is the one on field repairs. It's not that there is anything particularly difficult about field repairs; it's just that most experienced pilots will tell you that they never fly a damaged plane. If something happens in the field, they wait for an experienced mechanic to make repairs or check any field repairs before flying out. Once the plane has been competently examined and fixed properly, then it can be flown safely.

The best course of action is to never fly a damaged plane. If there is the slightest question in your mind as to the integrity of the plane, don't fly. It's just that simple. You always have a choice.

But there are times when you might want to make *minor* repairs in order to fly. Perhaps the damage is so slight that a simple repair will make the plane airworthy. Legendary bush pilot John Cross out of Kotzebue, for instance, once went down over the tundra when his gas line became clogged with mosquitoes. How did mosquitoes get into the gas supply? That's a question that John Cross couldn't answer to the day

Brian Nelson

Fig. 7-7. *Wing covers are important in snow country. If you have a choice, buy fluorescent ones. Why? because they will serve double duty as distress signals whether you place them on white snow or the dark ground of the forest or meadows.*

he died. Professional mechanics were few and far between in those days. When something went wrong with your plane, you fixed it yourself.

In more recent years, planes have been repaired in a variety of ways. One pilot had his plane attacked by grizzlies—while it was on the ground, of course. The bears were probably trying to get to some food they believed to be inside the aircraft. After they had given up, the structure of the plane was fine but the skin was shredded. The pilot radioed his condition and asked for a few dozen rolls of carpet tape. When it arrived, he wrapped the tape around and around the fuselage until he had completely covered the ripped areas. (A photograph of the plane wrapped in tape can be found in the now defunct *Alaska Flying Magazine*, which you should be able to find in your local library.)

While it is not advisable to fly a damaged plane, for *minor* repairs you might wish to do in the field, below is a list of suggested items for a field repair kit. Once again, this is an advised list for people who wish to make *minor* repairs on a plane that still has its flying integrity intact.

- 40 feet of rope, nylon *not* hemp.
- 40 feet of wire.

you more power. STOL will also give you a slower stall speed because you are increasing your lift.

TAKEOFF AND LANDING SURFACES

If you plan on flying in Alaska, you had better get used to making landings on ice, gravel strips, and lakes. All of these surfaces can be tricky. But as long as you depend more on horse sense than horsepower, you won't have any trouble.

Ice landings, particularly, can be very tricky. (*See* Chapter 3.) The rule of thumb is have at least a foot of solid ice before you attempt to land. This, however, is a bit sticky because you can't judge the thickness of the ice from the air. Worse, just because it is cold enough in Anchorage or Fairbanks to freeze the lakes one foot thick does not mean that every lake in between these two cities is one foot thick as well.

Additionally, lakes and rivers vary in ice thickness as well. Bodies of water do not ice up uniformly. Shore ice forms first, where the water is the shallowest, and then the ice shelves out as the temperature drops, the thinnest ice being in the center of the lake. As the temperature continues to drop, the ice thickens.

To complicate matters, this is only true for a normal, circular lake. Unfortunately, the only body of water in Alaska that is circular is a pothole in Spenard. Odd-shaped lakes dot the landscapes; rivers add idiosyncrasies to ponds. Upwellings, warm springs, outlets, inlets, and swift-moving waters can keep the ice from freezing to a foot thick, so there is no way to be absolutely sure that ice is at least a foot thick.

Landing on ice is also difficult because you really don't have that much control of the plane. You *will* skid. Even with wheels, your brakes won't work well. If you are planning on putting down on ice, choose a nice long landing area. You'll probably need it.

While there are some bush pilots who say that landing on snow and ice with pontoons is acceptable because "ice and snow are just frozen water," it's not a good idea. Floats are made for real water, not frozen water. Even pontoons with wheels are not a good idea in winter. Play it safe; when winter comes, use skis or wheels (FIG. 5-12). Use the pontoons if you are flying in Hawaii.

When you take off from an icefield or snowfield, be sure to use the same tracks to get out that you used to come in. You have already packed the snow so there is an established trail. Second, if you had no problem coming in, there is no reason to assume you will have problems getting out.

If you have to pack your trail, be extremely careful. Since you will most likely be using your plane's skis, don't let the plane go too fast. Light snow will hide ground obstacles. Don't discover them the hard way. Many Alaskan pilots keep a pair of snowshoes for exactly this purpose. You can pack a trail with skis, but snowshoes make it a lot easier. But packing a trail with skis is unquestionably easier than doing it in boots alone.

If you are packing down an area where you did not land, be careful and look for the signs of thin ice: variations in the ice color, a sheen of water on the surface, or swamp creatures rising out of a huge hole in the ice and reaching for your skis.

SNOWSHOES

87

- • 40 FT OF ROPE
- • 40 FT OF WIRE
- Two pair of vise grips of different sizes.
- Pliers.
- Two adjustable wrenches (English).
- Hacksaw with three blades.
- Rubber hammer.
- Steel hammer.
- Set of screwdrivers, Regular and Phillips.
- Small bottle of Windex and a roll of paper towels.
- Can of PAM.
- Can of WD40.
- Several rolls of duct and/or aluminum tape.
- Extra radio fuses.
- Pair of gloves.
- Soldering kit.
- ~~Book of waterproof matches~~. STRIKE ANY WHERE MATCHES
- Hatchet.

There are a wide variety of field repairs that pilots have alleged they have used to keep their planes airworthy. None of these alleged cures are recommended by the authors or publisher but are included in this book simply for the entertainment of the readers.

One well-known bush pilot stated that when he hit hard, he bent one blade of his propeller so badly that it was unusable. He had a hacksaw in his aircraft so he removed the portion of the prop that was bent and shortened the other blade appropriately. Though he lost a lot of power, he was able to fly out of the bush.

A pilot who had a leak in his pontoon beached his aircraft and elevated the damaged float. When it was empty, he blocked the holes from the *inside* of the pontoon with birch bark rolls. Then he braced the birch bark with sticks and filled the bottom portion of the float with sand. The sticks and the sand held the bark in place which, in turn, made the float useable for one takeoff and landing.

After a particularly brutal landing, one pilot found that a portion of one wing tip had been sheared off. After he examined the wing carefully, he decided that there might be minor damage within the wing itself. With a hatchet he felled a small sapling, trimmed the branches, and rammed the spar inside his wing for added strength. He left the top of the sapling untouched, however, to serve as the tip of the damaged wing.

After some damage was sustained by his landing gear, a pilot took a moose rack and strapped it to the struts to allow for extra support. It was enough to allow him to land in Anchorage.

When a tire blew out landing on a remote landing strip, a pilot cut a larger hole in the rubber and jammed towels, shirts, and an old jacket into the interior. The plane "limped a lot" but took off safely.

Fig. 7-8. *Planes do crash. Be prepared. Every time you get into your plane, make certain that you have the gear to allow you to survive on the ground.*

Regardless of how you repair your plane, keep in mind that you are responsible. If something goes wrong with one of your repair jobs, you are the one to pay the price for that error. If you are carrying passengers, their lives are in your hands as well.

Finally, in terms of repairs, remember that even if your plane has been repaired by a qualified, competent, experienced mechanic, you are still responsible for his repairs. This means that you check *all* of the repair work done on your aircraft. Even if you trust the mechanic with your life, don't trust him or her to check the work. That's your responsibility. If something goes wrong while you are in the air—that's your responsibility as well (FIG. 7-8).

8
Staying Alive After the Plane Has Gone Down

ALL RIGHT. THE WORST THAT COULD POSSIBLY HAPPEN HAS HAPPENED. Your plane has gone down. You hit hard—real hard. No one is bleeding, but everyone is shaken—badly. Both wings have been sheared off, and the tail has snapped free of the fuselage. Unfortunately, all of your survival gear was in the tail section and it is now sitting in 10 feet of 35 °F water. Now comes the good news. It will be dark in an hour and you didn't file a flight plan (FIGS. 8-1, 8-2, and 8-3). It is starting to rain, the temperature is dropping, and a lot of cumulonimbus clouds are sweeping in from the north.

If you learn nothing else from this book, make absolutely, positively sure you understand this next sentence: *Your chances of survival depend on staying warm and dry*. Scores of books on the market prattle on about how to build snares, what bushes to eat, how to butcher a rabbit, and how to fish with primitive, makeshift hooks and sinkers. That's nice information to fill out a survival book, but the bottom line is still the same: *Your chances of survival depend on staying warm and dry*.

It was incredibly stupid of you not to have filed a flight plan. People die for making a mistake like that. But there's not much that you can do about it now. The first thing for you to do is to calculate when you will be missed. If you were off on a three-day fishing trip and were on your way back when you went down, you can expect a rescue plane out within a few hours. That's because most people file flight plans and are expected at each leg of the journey. What does this statistic mean to you? *Don't spend your time wandering around*. Stay dry. Stay warm. Stay in a shelter. Good things come to those who wait. Spend your time waiting.

Form Approved OMB No 2120-0026

| U.S DEPARTMENT OF TRANSPORTATION FEDERAL AVIATION ADMINISTRATION

FLIGHT PLAN	(FAA USE ONLY) ☐ PILOT BRIEFING ☐ VNR ☐ STOPOVER		TIME STARTED	SPECIALIST INITIALS

| 1 TYPE

VFR

IFR

DVFR | 2. AIRCRAFT IDENTIFICATION | 3. AIRCRAFT TYPE/ SPECIAL EQUIPMENT | 4. TRUE AIRSPEED

KTS | 5. DEPARTURE POINT | 6. DEPARTURE TIME

PROPOSED (Z) | ACTUAL (Z) | 7. CRUISING ALTITUDE |

8. ROUTE OF FLIGHT

| 9 DESTINATION (Name of airport and city) | 10 EST. TIME ENROUTE

HOURS | MINUTES | 11. REMARKS |

| 12 FUEL ON BOARD

HOURS | MINUTES | 13. ALTERNATE AIRPORT(S) | 14. PILOT'S NAME, ADDRESS & TELEPHONE NUMBER & AIRCRAFT HOME BASE | 15. NUMBER ABOARD |

17. DESTINATION CONTACT/TELEPHONE (OPTIONAL)

| 16 COLOR OF AIRCRAFT | CIVIL AIRCRAFT PILOTS. FAR Part 91 requires you file an IFR flight plan to operate under instrument flight rules in controlled airspace. Failure to file could result in a civil penalty not to exceed $1,000 for each violation (Section 901 of the Federal Aviation Act of 1958, as amended). Filing of a VFR flight plan is recommended as a good operating practice. See also Part 99 for requirements concerning DVFR flight plans. |

FAA Form 7233-1 (8-82)   **CLOSE VFR FLIGHT PLAN WITH_____ FSS ON ARRIVAL**

Figs. 8-1 and 8-2. *These pieces of paper can save your life. Make sure you file all information needed. Take the extra 30 seconds at the desk rather than risk your life on the ground.*

⊙ CHEAP SPACE BLANKETS ARE THE BEST SIGNALING DEVICES.

There are three or four things you should do immediately—after you have made sure that no one needs medical attention. If you have wing covers on board, pull them out and spread them on the ground. This will give you better visibility from the air, particularly if your wing covers are red or fluorescent. (This is a strong hint to buy red or fluorescent wing covers when you need your next pair.)

Once the wing covers are spread out, check your ELT (FIG. 8-4). *Do not assume that the ELT is on and operating just because you have impacted the ground. Check it out.* Keep in mind that the ELT works on forward G forces. In other words, if the ELT was moving *forward* and stopped very suddenly—with a force of more than 6 Gs (six times the force of gravity)—then the transmitter should be operating. But, if the plane went up on its nose, flipped, and slid backwards, the ELT would probably not have been triggered.

If you can take the ELT out of the plane, do so. You will notice that there is a strap of metal around the transmitter. Pull this free—*carefully*—and place one end of the metal between the antenna contact points. Then set the ELT someplace secure where the metal strip will not fall free of the contact points.

If you cannot get the ELT out of the plane, check the antenna. Does it look serviceable? Can you actually see the antenna? If the antenna does not look serviceable or you cannot see it, take some wire and attach it to the base of the ELT antenna hous-

124

FLIGHT LOG

DEPARTURE POINT	VOR		RADIAL	DISTANCE		TIME			GROUND SPEED
	IDENT.	TO		LEG	POINT-POINT		TAKEOFF		
	FREQ.		FROM	REMAINING	CUMULATIVE				
CHECK POINT							ETA		
							ATA		
DESTINATION									
				TOTAL					

PREFLIGHT CHECK LIST

DATE

EN ROUTE WEATHER/WEATHER ADVISORIES

DESTINATION WEATHER

WINDS ALOFT

ALTERNATE WEATHER

FORECASTS

NOTAMS/AIRSPACE RESTRICTIONS

Fig. 8-2.

FLIGHT PLAN FORMAT

FAST FILE 263-6597 TWEB 276-8199 PILOT BRIEFING 276-1929

1. TYPE OF FLIGHT PLAN - VFR-DVFR-IFR	10. ESTIMATED TIME ENROUTE HRS
2. AIRCRAFT IDENT N_____	MINS
3. AIRCRAFT TYPE & SPECIAL EQUIPMENT	11. REMARKS
4. TRUE AIRSPEED	12. FUEL ON BOARD HRS
5. POINT OF DEPARTURE	MINS
6. DEPARTURE TIME (PROPOSED_____ACTUAL_____)	13. ALTERNATE AIRPORTS
7. INITIAL CRUISING ALTITUDE	14. PILOTS NAME, ADDRESS, & PHONE
8. ROUTE OF FLIGHT	15. NUMBER ABOARD
9. DESTINATION	16. COLOR OF AIRCRAFT

ANCHORAGE FSS/IFSS

Fig. 8-3. *When you file your flight plan by radio, follow the instructions.*

Brian Nelson

Fig. 8-4. *Handheld, portable ELT.*

ing and extend it into the air. You may not be doing much but, in your current circumstances, "not much" might still be enough to give you that extra edge.

Now, while this is an incredibly stupid bit of advice, it is nonetheless critical. Is the ELT turned on? Check it to make sure. If you don't know how to check the ELT, look at the photograph in this section that shows the ELT in the ON position. If you have a handheld radio, use it (FIG. 8-5).

Fig. 8-5. *Handheld communication radio.*

Brian Nelson

Your next course of action is to make a shelter. It's starting to rain, so you'd better be quick. Find the driest ground possible. If you are in a swamp, look for dry ground. If that is not reasonable, see if you can use the plane as a foundation. But get off the wet ground.

See if you can lift one of the wings across some boulders, fallen trees, or the gutted fuselage for a makeshift shelter. If the plane is not usable, use its aluminum skin. Rip the skin free, collect the largest pieces, and stack them on top of the wing. Forget what you read about chopping down trees and making a shelter with the boughs. You will probably have all the material you need from your own plane.

If you want to get some use from the hatchet in your survival kit, hack off some heavy boughs and lay them across the loose pieces of aluminum. Put rocks on the aluminum if you have to, which may be necessary since there is a storm coming. Those pieces of metal are all that's standing between you and the storm. Plan your lean-to carefully; it's the difference between life and death.

Once the heavy work has been done on the lean-to, send someone out to gather firewood. The lean-to will keep you dry; now find a fuel source to keep you warm. But you haven't got much time. It's going to be dark soon.

Forget about chopping wood into kindling. Forget about making a pile of small twigs and a pile of limbs and a pile of logs. Get as much wood as you can as quickly as you can. If you have the option, put some of the wood—at least the smaller pieces—in the lean-to. Sleep on it if necessary. That's to start your fire in the morning if you need it.

If you have time, roll some rocks into a fire circle. Be a good scout and make sure that you are not going to start a forest fire. (Then you might not want to be found.) The fire circle is also critical for a number of other reasons.

First, you want to construct a fire circle with large rocks at the back so that the heat will bounce into the lean-to. You can't have the fire in the lean-to, but you can make a fire pit in such a way that the heat bounces into the shelter.

Second, without an axe, you are going to have to burn the larger logs in two-foot sections, moving more of the log into the fire as it burns. The circle of rocks will allow you to keep the logs from falling into the coals. You need those coals because they will blast heat into the shelter all night long. Keeping the logs off the coals will dry the wood out without putting out the coals, and allow the wood to burn longer.

To start the fire, use whatever paper you have. Dollar bills, business cards, and whatever else you have in your wallet or purse can be used. Use the pages of this book. Use some of the pages from your Red Cross First Aid Book or your survival manual. (You did put one of each of these into your plane, didn't you?) Kindling and wood shavings are fine, but from personal experience, even seasoned campers have a difficult time getting a camp fire started—particularly if the wood is wet.

Be very, very, very careful about starting a fire using avgas. You should also be very careful about getting too close to the fire. Some gas might have accidentally sprayed onto your clothing. Smell your sleeves before starting the fire.

Until it gets dark, collect firewood. Once it's dark, get into the lean-to and stay there. Sleep as much as you can, but make sure that at least one person is up at all times to watch the fire.

The moment it is light enough to see, immediately begin foraging for firewood. Even if it is raining lightly, get the firewood. You are going to need it. If the sky is so heavily overcast and the rain coming down so hard that no one is flying, it doesn't make much sense to start your fires. Use your best judgment. As soon as the weather starts to clear, get those fires started.

If you are in the mountains, look for the highest reasonable area for the fire. This does not mean putting on climbing gear and attacking a precipice. It *does* mean that if you see a bald spot on the mountain a half mile away, go for it. Put your signal fires there, not down in the forest. But don't take any risks to get the fires going as far up as you can. The climb may be tiring, but it could make your rescue easier.

You will probably attract more attention during the day with a smoky fire so throw on anything that will cause smoke. Oily rags are good, so are green branches and grasses. The smoke will also keep the insects away. At night, just stick to wood.

You should also start exposing as much metal on the ground as you can. The more items there are that can reflect light, the better. Spread your clothing out in the sunshine—if there is sunshine and your clothes are a different color than the background. *Anything* you can do to make your encampment stand out from the background is in your favor.

Now, just in case you have to walk out, start thinking ahead. If you do not have any insect repellent, start smoking your clothes. Really saturate them with smoke. It may not work as well as bug juice or mosquito netting, but it won't hurt (FIG. 8-6).

Fig. 8-6. *One of the most important survival items is insect repellent.*

Brian Nelson

You should also start putting together a survival kit (FIG. 8-7). Choose the components of this kit carefully. Pull out wires to use as snare lines. Snap off mirrors to use for signaling. If you have any plastic film containers, throw away the film and stuff the container with rags soaked in gas. This will help you start a fire. Clean any containers you can find so you can carry water.

If conditions warrant, you may want to carry some coals with you. If the plane came down on dry ground, thank your lucky stars. Most of Alaska is wet. Very wet. You may need those coals to start a fire if the wood at your next campsite is wet. Though you may feel like someone out of *Quest for Fire*, if it saves your life, savor the comparison.

WALKING OUT

If you have really screwed up, there will come a time when you have to make the choice of staying or walking out. This is not a decision to be made lightly or without thinking; your life is in the balance.

Fig. 8-7. *Inventory survival equipment, which frequently includes wing covers.*

The general rule of thumb is that your chances of being rescued are better if you stay with your plane. But if you didn't file a flight plan and are not expected back for a week and are in a remote area and have been putting up signal fires for five days, maybe you should think about packing out.

But before you start, leave a note in the plane saying where you are going and when you left. Sooner or later someone is going to discover that plane. If a rescue party arrives the day after you leave, it would be nice if they knew where to start looking. Think of this note as the flight plan you didn't file.

Do not take apart your shelter. If the country gets rough, you may find that you have no choice but to return. Further, if your plane is found and you were foolish enough to leave your camp without writing a note, the shelter will show that there were survivors.

If you have to start walking out, stick to game trails if there are any. If not, stay on dry ground. Even if you have to backtrack, stay on dry ground. Again, your chief concern is staying warm and dry.

While many survival books show you how to navigate by the stars, that's fine if you are on a plain and know where civilization is. In Alaska, precise directions may help you, but in most cases, you can't just walk over the horizon and find a community.

If you are in the mountains, see if you spot a river before you get down. That's where you will be heading. Keep an eye out for "swamp trees," the scraggly evergreens that grow in the wetlands. (Those are black spruce, by the way.) When you see them in the distance, steer clear of the area. If you find a stream, follow it. Remember, keep heading in a downstream direction. Sooner or later you will come to a community, albeit a small one.

If you are not in a position to see the countryside laid out before you, choose a direction and stick to it. Use a compass, don't trust to the sun. In Alaska, the sun circles the sky so don't expect to get a good fix on what is east and what is west.

If you can see the stars, find the Big Dipper. Then, follow a hypothetical line from the last two stars on the dipper's cup to the North Star. Once you have found the North Star, obviously, you know where north is. Now, choose your direction of travel. If you know where the nearest community is, head in that direction. If you don't have the slightest idea where you are and where the nearest community is, head south. That's probably the best general advice.

If you decide to go south, make sure you keep moving in that direction. Do not wander all over the map. Sure, move around swamps and lakes, but keep heading south. Make sure that you state in the note you left that you are heading south.

Finally, be sure to light a fire every night. Not only will it serve to keep you warm and dry, but it will be easy to see at night. And, should you be lucky and make it out alive, don't ever leave the ground again without filing a flight plan.

WINTER SURVIVAL

Surviving in winter can be a bit dicier. On the plus side, landing in snow can enhance your chances of surviving the initial impact and, if you have to hike out, you will be able to travel much faster. Lighting signal fires is a bit more difficult because wood is hard to find under the snow but, on the upside, because there is so much darkness, the signal fires are visible for miles. It's easier for rescue planes to get in and out of remote areas because the planes can use skis. Animals are easier to track and there are no large omnivores out and around.

On the downside, however, it's a lot colder. Storms can drop the temperatures well below zero and blow for days at a time.

Once again, the bottom line for survival in winter is the same as for summer. Stay warm and dry. Drink as much water as you can. Build your shelter as soon as possible and forage for wood.

Water is a bit easier to find. Put some snow in a plastic bag and tuck it inside your parka. Let your body heat turn the snow to water.

The rules for survival in the winter are the same as those for the summer. Wait. Be patient. Don't take risks. Keep warm and dry. The only difference is that if you have to walk out, make yourself snowshoes first.

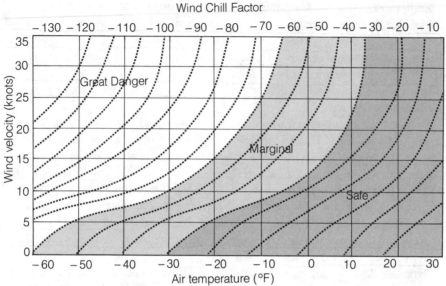

Fig. 8-8. *The combination of ambient temperature and wind velocity produces the wind chill index. To estimate wind chill, go across the table at the bottom to find the air temperature. Then go straight up to the appropriate wind velocity. Finally, follow the curved lines upwards to the top of the chart. There you can read the estimated equivalent temperature in degrees. The wind chill is more pronounced if you are wet. Adapted from the National Search and Rescue Manual*

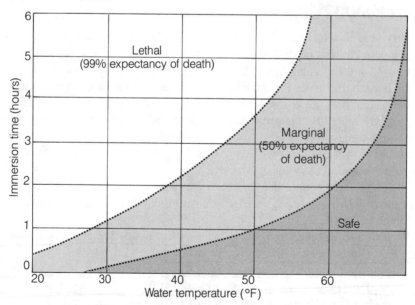

Fig. 8-9. *Prolonged immersion in warmer waters as well as shorter immersions in cold water can be lethal. Adapted from National Search and Rescue Manual*

ONCE YOU HAVE BEEN RESCUED

Once you have been spotted, take a few moments before you fly home. Collect your wing covers and *turn off your ELT*. Now that you are safe, don't put anyone else at risk. If you fly out and forget to turn the ELT off, someone else might pick up your distress signal and assume that you are still in need of assistance. Turning off the ELT means that someone else is not going to risk their life searching for you after you have been rescued (FIGS. 8-8 and 8-9).

9
Alive, Dead, and Dangerous Cargo

IT ALL STARTED IN THE DARKEST DAYS OF THE GREAT DEPRESSION. MONEY was tight and everyone in Alaska, pilots and herring squeezers alike, were working hard scrambling quickly for any dollars they could find. Against this historical and financial backdrop, it came to pass, that an old fisherman died in Dutch Harbor. Being halfway out on the Aleutian Chain, it didn't make sense to transport the body back to the mainland, so the authorities did what was usual in such a case. They buried the body, searched the personal effects of the individual, and contacted any relatives whose name appeared on letters or legal documents.

In the case of this fisherman, the burial could not come too soon. He had died of what the medical professionals in Dutch Harbor called a "complicated internal condition" which, considering the skill of the medical practitioners in Dutch Harbor, could have been anything relating to internal organs. The fact that the body was emitting a high level of stink was the reason for burying the body as soon as possible.

In the process of searching the fisherman's last effects, the authorities discovered a will in which the elderly man left his entire estate, some $75,000 ($1.4 million today), to a niece in Seattle. The niece, who had probably never even met the codger, became instantly and sentimentally attached to the old man.

Not wanting such a valuable member of the family to be buried in an unmarked grave in a remote community, she decided to have his remains brought back to Washington. But she wanted the corpse to return in style. The barge was too slow, so the niece offered a large cash reward in the thousands-of-dollars range to any pilot who could arrange transportation of the body back to Seattle.

As a result, there was a "corpse rush" to Dutch Harbor. The first pilot to arrive on the windswept island was Alex Holden of Alaska Southern Airways. Holden, however, was in for a shock. He had not been told of the condition of body at death or that it had been buried. Holden wired his boss for instructions and received a cable that was short, succinct and left no doubt as to its intent: "Get the body." This one trip meant $2,000 cash, about $40,000 in today's dollars, to the struggling Alaskan Southern Airways.

Wiring the courthouse, most likely in Seward, Holden got a court order to exhume the body. As quickly as possible, for very good reason, the corpse was wrapped in canvas and given several heavy coats of shellac. When the shellac dried, Holden had a modern-day mummy.

However, while the mummy of the Egyptian empire came with its sarcophagus, Holden was not so lucky. Only after the body had stiffened rigid did Holden discover that the corpse would not fit inside the plane. (Even if it had, the stench would have made the journey unbearable.) After he had exhausted all other possibilities, Holden strapped the corpse onto the wing of his plane and flew it to Seward where a coffin was waiting. From there, the coffin went by ferry and rail to Seattle.

While not all Alaska air cargo stories are as unusual as the tale of Alex Holden and the corpse, Alaska has more than its fair share of stories. This is primarily because one-third of the people of Alaska live in what is called the "bush." This defines all areas that are not connected to Anchorage or Fairbanks by road. For these residents, goods and supplies come by barge during the summer—all 100 ice-free days of it north of the Arctic Circle—or by plane during the rest of the year. Fuel, automobiles, and other large objects have to be brought in by barge. Everything else must come in by plane.

And there, Shakespeare would have said, is the rub. The weight of freight, alas and unfortunately, is often judged on the basis of the number of trips that will be required rather than the poundage. Many bush pilots see if they can trim the number of trips down. This, of course, saves on time and fuel. What it also does is risk your life.

OVERLOADING

The greatest danger, as aircraft crash inspectors say, is that overloading "sneaks up on you." For instance, many pilots have a tendency to stuff the plane. They know what the safe load limits are, but, well, you know, they could put just one more box on board. "Sure, the plane will be a little sluggish taking off and probably hit a little hard coming in but, gee, it's just another box. It would be a shame to have to fly all the way back here just to pick up one box." So the box goes onboard. And nothing happens.

Then comes step two. If you can slip one extra box onboard and it doesn't cause much of a problem, then why not two or three? The exception now becomes the rule. Now, rather than just flying slightly overloaded, the plane is continually flying well over recommended limits.

While the pilot is scooting along through the sky feeling calm and confident that all is well, what is actually happening is that his stall speed has been increased. To keep the craft aloft, he will have to make the approaches at a higher rate of speed; he will need more runway to land.

If the pilot continues to overload his plane, one of three things will eventually occur. First, if the runway is too short or the plane lands too far down the runway, the weight of the plane will carry it off the end of the runway. On many airstrips in Alaska this is fatal.

This is not unusual, considering the average length of a runway in Alaska is 2,500 feet. But that's the average; and a lot of landings are done on sandbars, gravel roads (between bends), or ice. Anchorage International Airport might be more than 10,000 feet long, but that is the exception, not the rule.

Second, if the plane is overloaded and is going too slow on its approach to the airstrip, it will, quite literally, fall out of the sky. This will not be too bad if the stall speed is reached when the plane is four or five feet off the runway, but if stall speed is reached when the plane is 2 miles from the runway over water or rugged terrain, the result could be fatal.

Third, a pilot could jump aboard an overloaded plane, gun his engine, and then try to take off. But because the plane is overloaded it is going to require a lot more distance to take off. That could be very expensive real estate if the pilot should run out of runway before he is off the ground. Hitting a forest at 60 mph is not good for a pilot's health, wealth, or mental well-being.

Overloading should not be a problem with commercial flights. Every carrier has strict weight guidelines. Personnel are specifically hired to make sure that the plane is not overloaded. Freight is weighed before it is put onboard and adjusted with the weight of the passengers.

The biggest problem comes with the noncommercial carriers. Usually these are the Sunday pilots who rarely carry any freight at all. They decide to go hunting, rent a Beaver, and drop a moose. They eyeball the moose, guess it weighs 800 pounds, estimate that the hunters and their gear weigh another 600. Six and eight is 14, so they think they have a 100-pound edge. They figure they're being conservative and say, "fine, let's shag."

However, the problem is that the moose is pushing 1,200 and both hunters weigh 225 apiece and are carrying 300 pounds of gear. That's 1,950 pounds, 450 over the safe limit for the Beaver. They give themselves a little extra room for the takeoff and make it off the water—and into the trees at the far end of the lake.

Another freight problem that quite a few bush pilots bring upon themselves is not packing their freight properly (FIG. 9-1). They toss boxes into the plane, squeeze them where they have to, and pile more on top. Or, rather than packing for weight and balance, they pack functionally. If they are going to make three stops, they pack the material for the last stop first and the first stop last. This makes it easy to unload but could unbalance the plane. That's bad for flying and hard when the plane lands.

Fig. 9-1. *Bob Reeve loading a boiler the hard way.*

Then there's the actual placement of material in the aircraft (FIGS. 9-2 and 9-3). Sometimes Blazo or Sterno is not packed properly for transport. (It should be tied to the inside of the plane or wedged in so it won't roll around.) If the plane goes down, the cans could rupture and what was a survivable aircraft accident turns into a fatality when the plane erupts into a fireball.

For some people, cargo is not something that is off loaded. It is dropped. While in the Lower 48, dropping cargo is unthinkable; in Alaska, it is not only common but, in many cases, is the common sense way to get cargo delivered on time and on target.

Wintertime, of course, is the best time to drop cargo—unless, of course, you use a parachute, which could turn out to be as expensive as the cargo itself. But during the winter, the deep snow cushions the fall and the cargo arrives intact. Sometimes it doesn't matter what the condition of the cargo is when it hits the ground. The United States Coast Guard, for instance, usually delivers Christmas trees to its far-flung LORAN bases in Alaska by dropping them out of C-130s. The trees aren't hurt because their shape makes them, aerodynamically speaking, like giant feathers. Well, they are a bit heavier than feathers, but the principle is the same.

When dropping cargo, it is extremely important to do it right the first time. This means that the person doing the dropping knows exactly what is to be done and does not endanger himself in dumping the cargo out the back of a Beaver.

Before any load is dropped, do a fly-by. Because you are going to be dropping into a snowfield, figure out where your load will land. You can do this by attaching a wide

138

Fig. 9-2. *Load your plane carefully to make certain your cargo does not shift while you are in the air.*

Fig. 9-3. *Note the snowshoes in the plane. This pilot is loading the aircraft correctly. He is taking into consideration weight and balance as well as ease of access when he gets to where he is going. Packing your snowshoes at the bottom of your cargo makes no sense at all—unless it is the middle of the summer.*

ribbon onto a stick or rock and tossing it out as you make your fly-by. Watch the ribbon as it falls. Is there any indication of wind? Did it land where you wanted it to?

Because you are going to need a partner, make absolutely sure you have your signals straight. If you want to know why, ask Doug Geeting. One Christmas while he was supplying a number of mountain climbers on Mt. McKinley—or Mt. Denali, depending on how congress acts on the name change legislation—Geeting received an order for a halibut. Halibut? That's right, even mountain climbers like fish.

Working with an inexperienced cargo handler, Geeting set out for Mt. McKinley with the requested halibut and an assortment of other goods for other groups of climbers scattered up the mountain. When he arrived at the first encampment, the crew that had ordered the halibut, he turned to his cargo thrower-outer and yelled "Halibut."

She, however, thought he said "All of it." So she threw all of it out the open door. It rained supplies on the mountain climbers. The frozen hunk of halibut hit a tent and ripped it in two. A case of beer landed between two men inside another tent spraying the men. Other supplies pockmarked the landscape, giving the campsite the appearance of a bomb-testing range.

Feeling the plane unexpectedly light, Geeting turned around to see what was going on. When he saw the cargo bay empty he asked what had happened.

"I threw it out," his cargo handler said. "You said, 'All of it.'"

"No, I said 'Halibut!'" Then he turned his Beaver and went back to see what kind of damage had been done. But as he approached the campsite, he saw everyone scattering. They thought he was making a return run!

EXTERNAL LOADS

Another danger many bush pilots seem blissfully ignorant of is the impact of external loads on aerodynamics. While it is possible to get an FAA permit for external loads, getting a permit does not make it safe.

The biggest problem with external loads, aircraft safety people say over and over again, is that whatever you load will necessarily make you an experimental test pilot. The aerodynamics have been changed. While strapping a set of canoes to the pontoon struts of a Beaver may be common and won't cause much of a problem, binding sheets of plywood to your struts will definitely cause a change in how the plane flies. It will get even worse if there happens to be a wind blowing.

If you have to fly with an external load, think about your cargo before you strap it onboard. How will it affect airflow? How will it affect the balance of the plane? What happens, for example, if you strap three 15-foot beams on your wing? If there is trouble, can you get out of the aircraft? If you can't, you should not be making the run with the oversized cargo.

ANIMALS

Flying animals in the round, so to speak, takes a special type of pilot. While a dog in a live-animal crate is no particular problem, unrestrained animals are. The best advice for flying with unrestrained animals is don't.

This advice was learned the hard way by an Alaskan pilot (who did not want his name used) out of Homer. One night he received a radio message to pick up a fare on the far side of Kachemak Bay. When he got there he discovered that his passenger had a cat on her lap. The pilot said he had a policy of taking no live animals, pets or otherwise. The lady said she was going to go to Homer with her cat and that was that.

Thereafter, there ensued a lively discussion that was resolved with the lady absolutely, positively guaranteeing that the cat was "plane broken" and would have no trouble on the short hop over to Homer. "She's made the trip many times before," the pilot was assured.

Well, that apparently was not the case. At 3,000 feet, halfway across Kachemak Bay, the cat suddenly went berserk. It exploded out of the woman's lap and began running around the inside of the plane as if it were the inside of a county fair motorcycle daredevil chamber. "And it was yowling to beat the devil, too," he said.

As the cat rounded the windshield for the third time, the pilot opened his door and, in the next instant, the cat was gone. "Just enforcing my no pet rule," the pilot commented. The lady was not pleased.

Dogs are not much better than cats. Ask Alaska bush pilot Cliff Hudson. As a favor, he was transporting his friend's dog when the plane went through some heavy weather. Though Hudson didn't have any trouble, the dog was quite distressed. The dog was so distressed, in fact, that it started jumping around. Its foot hit the door and handle and, in the next instant, the dog had jumped out of the plane and disappeared into the clouds.

There wasn't much that Hudson could say to his buddy except "Sorry." As soon as the weather cleared, the two men went back to look for the dog, that is, the dog's body. But when they landed, who should come bounding out of the forest but the dog. Apparently, the deep snow had cushioned his fall. The animal had a few scratches and a bruise or two, but other than that it was fine.

But they did have a hell of a time getting the dog back into the plane.

Other animals have caused pilots more than just a few gray hairs. Doug Geeting, Talkeetna glacier pilot and coauthor of *Mountain Flying*, tells of a program to fly grizzlies out of populated areas. The grizzlies were darted and, while they were asleep, they were flown to pastures "far from the madding crowds."

On one particular trip, the slumbering grizzly was not in as deep a repose as the fish and wildlife professionals had supposed. Halfway through the trip the slumbering bear regained a groggy consciousness for a few seconds. it started clawing at the back of Geeting's seat and pulling at the fuselage.

There were some tense moments, Geeting admits, and now he doesn't fly alone. If he carries a bear, a Fish and Wildlife person comes along—in the plane. Good advice from a man who has learned the hard way.

When flying with live animals, go to seemingly absurd lengths to keep the animals contained. Animals are unpredictable and if frightened can make it into the front of the aircraft and under the pilot's legs. Should an animal become rambunctious on the foot peddles, it could cause a great deal of unhappiness to all concerned.

PASSENGERS

It is very easy to say that Alaska has a dangerous rate of aircraft accidents. And that is true. When considering the per-capita accident rate, Alaska leads the nation. But what those statistics do not make clear is that Alaska is also the flyingest place in the country. It has the highest per-capita rate for pilots—one out of every eight Alaskans has a pilot's license.

Alaskans also depend more on the airplane than do the residents of any other state. Not only is it a necessity of travel, it is also a recreational requirement. Unlike other states, it is hard to get to the "outdoors" from the roads. Alaska has fewer than a handful of highways, and much of the land on either side is not fit for travel on foot. It's called wetlands. In the Lower 48, wetlands are known as swamps. This makes the airplane a necessity for hunters and fishermen.

What is the exception in the Lower 48 often becomes the rule in Alaska. In many bush communities, landing on a frozen lake is the way goods, supplies, and mail come in all winter. In California, not many pilots have ever landed on a frozen lake—at least not on purpose.

Landing on sandbars is not a common experience in the Lower 48 either. In Alaska, sometimes that is the only place to land. Landings such as these give new meaning to the term "breathe easier." Sandbars change from week to week, and each landing, as the air safety experts warn, "is a whole new experience."

What does this have to do with cargo? One of the most important, difficult, and demanding cargo to haul is people (FIG. 9-4). They talk and ask stupid questions. Worse, they can't be tied down, they fiddle with the instruments, and they require conversation. While many passengers are perfectly at home in the air, too many are not. Once off the ground they have to be constantly reassured that the engine is not going to rip itself out of the plane and that the wings will not vibrate themselves free of the fuselage. Passing through clouds frightens them, first, because they are absolutely sure that there is a mountain hidden in the folds of the cumulus and, second, because the plane jumps as the props chop through the cloud cover.

The best advice for dealing with unruly passengers is not to take them onboard in the first place. If you happen to be a flight-seeing pilot, you really don't have much option. You meet them for the first time five minutes before you take off. If they are bozos, you won't know until you are 3,000 feet up and one of them begins pestering

Brian Nelson

Fig. 9-4. *Double-check your passengers as well as your equipment before you take off. Don't get aloft and suddenly realize you have forgotten signal flares.*

you with inane questions. That's if you are lucky. If you are not lucky, one of your passengers will have claustrophobia, another gastric difficulties, and the two wives will keep up an incessant chatter that has nothing to do with the flightseeing trip at all.

When it comes to longer trips, such as flying hunters into recreational areas, you have a bit more time to eyeball your clients. Just as they have the right to choose to use you as their way into the bush, you also have the right to refuse them service. This is a right you should maintain.

Friend or fare-payer, look your passengers over with a critical eye before they get on board. Are these people dressed like cheechakos for a weekend in the wilderness? If the plane was forced to make an emergency landing, could these people make the night with what they are wearing?

Check out their shoes first. Anyone can buy a pair of Levi's and a plaid shirt and find a used pack at the Army-Navy Surplus store. But someone who really knows what it is like in the bush will come more prepared. Are they wearing boots or steel-toed waders? Are the boots new or do they show signs of use?

Another good sign is a knife. Does the person at least carry a knife? While outdoor experts say that one good pocketknife is more than adequate for camping, that's like saying that you only need one pan in your kitchen. If you don't see one on their belt, ask.

As a bare minimum, your passengers should have the following on their person:

- Knife, sheath knife.
- Waterproof matches.
- Plastic garbage bag.
- Handful of facial tissue or toilet paper.
- Hunting and/or fishing license if appropriate.

Further, your passengers should be dressed as if the plane *will* go down. That's not wishful thinking; that's reality. As every thinking-ahead pilot knows, there is always a chance that an emergency landing will have to be made. If that does happen, you could be on the ground for a while. Worse, the plane could be damaged so badly that no gear could be retrieved. Or the plane could catch on fire or sink in a lake, thereby depriving both pilot and passengers of survival equipment.

Finally, when dealing with passengers, make it crystal clear that *you are God* after the plane leaves the ground. Once they are in their seats, they are to stay there. Don't take chances.

This an example from the annals of Alaska's bush flying heritage. In the mid-1950s, a pilot was paid to transport a deranged woman from a small community. She seemed calm enough when she came onboard, so he did not order that she be secured to her seat. That was a mistake.

Halfway into town the woman suddenly rose from her seat, opened the back door of the plane, and stepped out before someone could stop her. Another passenger was able to catch her by one foot at the last moment and the patient hung out of the back of plane.

The passenger holding onto the foot yelled up to the pilot, "I can't hold onto this lady no more and I can't pull her back in, the wind is too strong."

Since the plane had wheels and the snow was too deep for the plane to land, the pilot began considering his options. They were both limited and fraught with disaster for the mental patient. Finally he took his best shot. Cutting back on his speed he descended and tipped the plane on its side. As low as he dared, he told the passenger to let go of the foot. The next instant the deranged woman was airborne. The pilot chose his spot well, for the woman landed in deep snow and was rescued a few hours later by a ground party. All she suffered were a few broken bones.

Glossary

ADF—Automatic direction finder. A black box that allows a pilot to home-in on a low/medium frequency radio station and navigate in that direction.

AGL—Above ground level.

air—The layers or blankets of molecules composed of 78% nitrogen, 21% oxygen, and 1% other gases that retain or release water vapors that are the basis for our weather.

ambient pressure—The pressure that exists outside. A pilot's ears, for instance, will adjust for the ambient pressure by popping.

assume—A very dangerous thing for a pilot to do.

atmosphere—That area extending up from the surface of the earth to 300 miles above the earth.

auto kinesis—An illusion in which lights will appear to move if the pilot stares at them for a number of minutes.

aviation bends—The bubbling of nitrogen in a pilot's or passenger's bloodstream as altitude is increased. This usually occurs when a pilot or passenger has been skin diving and all the pressurized nitrogen from the compressed air has not been released from the diver's body.

azimuth—A symbol on a map that looks like a circle that has been marked by degrees. Usually it indicates the location of a VOR* station.

bear insurance—A .357 Magnum.

black box—Any piece of equipment that helps the pilot but of whose internal workings the pilot knows nothing. Originally it meant supersecret navigational and firepower equipment that was removed from a fighter or bomber when the plane was on the runway. Today that definition has been expanded to refer to any equipment, like LORAN, which has intricate internal mechanisms but a simple exterior offering easy-to-read-and-interpret information.

black magic—What you depend upon when you don't do a preflight check before taking off.

carbon monoxide poisoning—Oxygen starvation of the human body caused by the intake of carbon monoxide. This condition usually occurs when exhaust fumes leak into the cockpit and poison the pilot before he knows he is in danger. Carbon Monoxide Poisoning is extremely dangerous because the pilot will black out before he knows he is in danger.

CAT—Clear air turbulence. Turbulence in what appears to be clear skies.

CDI—Course deviation indicator. The "left-right needle" that indicates if the plane is straying from its VOR station radial.

chinook—A sudden, warm wind in the middle of winter. It will start to melt the snow. A chinook, also called a warm snap, is dangerous to the pilot because it turns dry snow to wet snow.

cirrus cloud—High, streaked clouds ranging in altitude from 15,000 to 45,000 feet. These clouds are composed of ice crystals and are considered harbingers of bad weather though the storms may be hundreds of miles away. *See* mackerel sky.

cloud—The visual sign of moisture.

cold front—A mass of cold, moisture-laden air moving into an area. This usually means a storm and often winds as well.

cold snap—A sudden cooling trend that can drop the temperature scores of degrees overnight. *See* chinook.

condensation—The change of state of water from vapor to liquid.

Coriolis Effect—The gravitational powers that cause wind to rotate in a clockwise direction in the northern hemisphere and in a counterclockwise direction in the southern hemisphere.

Coriolus illusion—A condition in which it appears that the plane is rotating.

course selector—Also called an OBS (omni bearing selector). The OBS is the dial on the VOR indicator that indicates the VOR radial onto which the pilot has locked.

crabbing—What the wife of a hen-pecked husband does or, for the purposes of this book, the angling of the aircraft to correct for a crosswind.

crosswind—A wind that is blowing across your direction of travel. If it were blowing in your direction of travel, it would be called a tailwind. If it were blowing in the opposite direction, it would be called a headwind. A wind originating in the cockpit is called a breaking wind.

cumulus cloud—The traditional, puffy cotton clouds that may appear from 5,000 to 25,000 feet. They are often referred to as "fair weather clouds."

dew point—The point at which water vapor in the atmosphere will fall out as precipitation. *See* relative humidity.

DME—Distance measuring equipment. A black box that indicates the slant range in nautical miles between a plane and a responding VOR station.

elevator illusion—A condition in which the pilot feels that he is gaining or losing altitude even though the instruments do not show it.

ELT—Emergency locator transmitter. The ELT is a piece of survival gear that is required in all airplanes. It is activated when there is a forward G force of at least 6 G and it will operate for 72 hours. The signal will be picked up on 121.5 COM-RADIO, probably by a satellite. *See* forward G force.

eustachian tube—The connecting tube between the inner ear and the throat that allows the body to adjust the pressure of the inner ear to that of the ambient or outside pressure.

false horizon—An illusion in which the pilot sees a horizon that is not there.

featureless terrain illusion—An illusion that exists when there are no features on the terrain on which the pilot can focus his eyes. This would be like flying over miles and miles of ice sheet.

fog—Low lying clouds.

forward G force—A measurement of force moving in a forward direction. For example, an ELT works on the principle that an airplane crash will occur when the plane stops suddenly. Thus, the ELT is designed to be automatically triggered when the transmitter is moving forward and suddenly stops. This sudden stop after moving forward is known as "forward G force." G, in this case, means the force of gravity and, technically, the ELT will be triggered alive when the G force equals six.

freezing rain—An atmospheric condition caused by a temperature inversion. Moisture high in the atmosphere turns to rain and falls into a freezing zone. The rain then turns to freezing rain and, when it hits, it will freeze. *See* icing.

G—The force of gravity. On takeoff you can feel the G forces as you are pushed back into your seat. You can feel G forces being released when the plane decelerates and you feel yourself being pulled forward. *See* forward G force.

Gillam Weather—The worst possible weather imaginable. The term was made famous by Harold Gillam who would fly in any weather.

graveyard spin—A condition, aptly named, in which the pilot rotates the plane to the right but "feels" that the plane is rotating to the left. The pilot may rotate the plane the way he "feels" it should be and then go into a downward spin.

ground lighting illusion—A condition under which a pilot believes that car lights, street lights, or house lights are actually landing strip lights.

hail—Chunks of ice that are formed in the upper atmosphere that will only fall to earth when the pull of gravity exceeds the force of the wind bouncing the hail stones up.

hydroplaning—Unpredictable movement of a plane on a sheet of ice that has a sheen of water on top. Mechanically, what occurs is that the plane's tires are not actually on the solid surface of the ice but floating on a thin layer of water. Thus the wheels cannot "grab" the ice and, as a result, the aircraft will skim and slide to a stop. Hydroplaning can occur on a cement runway as well if there is a sheen of water that keeps the wheels from grabbing the surface.

hyperventilation—The intake of too much oxygen, which can result in giddiness and blacking out.

hypothermia—A physical condition in which the body loses heat. If this condition is sustained, the person will die of "exposure."

hypoxia—Oxygen starvation. A condition a pilot may encounter at higher altitudes where the oxygen level is thin.

ice crispies—Ice that is so eroded by spring conditions that it is honeycombed with galleries. Ice in this condition will not support the weight of an airplane. It is called ice crispies because when sheets of this ice break off and collide with the shore, the sound is not unlike that of the snap-crackle-pop cereal.

icing—When moisture hits an airplane, usually in the form of freezing rain, sticks, and turns to ice. This is a dangerous condition, as the icing adds weight to the airplane.

illusions—Believing that you see something that is not there.

inversion—An atmospheric condition where the temperature sequence is reversed. In other words, in normal circumstances, temperatures decline as the pilot rises in altitude. With an inversion, there is a blanket of cold temperature on the earth but higher up, the temperatures are much warmer, maybe scores of degrees warmer. *See* icing.

inversion illusion—A condition in which the pilot feels that he is leaning too far backwards during periods of rapid acceleration or takeoffs. Pilots suffering from this illusion will push their noses down, which could cause other problems.

ionosphere—The highest level of the atmosphere, which is 140 to 300 miles off the surface of the earth and the domain of the Aurora Borealis.

isobars—The line drawings on a weather map by which weather movements are charted and presented graphically.

lead—An open water area or break between two sheets of ice. A lead can appear in either fall or spring.

leans—An illusion that a pilot may feel when he feels that his plane is not flying level even though his instruments tell him that he is flying level. The pilot will be tempted to disregard his instruments and adjust the plane so that it "feels" right. This can lead to disaster.

left-right needle—Also known as a CDI, course deviation indicator. Once a VOR has locked onto a radial, the left-right needle will indicate whether the plane is on course.

line-of-sight mechanism—Usually in reference to a navigational or communication system, the term means that there has to be an unobstructed line between the transmitter and receiver. If a plane, for instance, was behind a mountain, the VOR would not work. As soon as the plane rose above the peak of the mountain, the VOR would receive an unobstructed signal and operate effectively again.

linear discrepancy—The variation of distance between what the instrument reads and what the actual facts are. For instance, in the case of a VOR, at a distance of 60 miles from the VOR station, the stream of electrons that compose a radial are one mile wide. While a pilot may assume that he is on course because his CDI indicates that he is, in actuality he could be two miles away.

LORAN—Acronym for Long Range Aid to Navigation. The United States Coast Guard currently operates LORAN stations around the world. Established in networks of threes, a LORAN communicator in a plane can triangulate its position. The accuracy of the LORAN signal is so refined that its variation is only one foot for each mile.

low pressure—An area where cold air is falling to earth. This is opposed to thermals, which is an area where warm air is rising. *See* thermals and high pressure.

mackerel sky—A sheet of high altitude cirrus clouds that appear as a wide band of fish scales.

mechanical turbulence—Turbulence caused by an immovable object, like a mountain range.

millibar—The unit of measurement of the pressure of the atmosphere, i.e., the amount of pressure of the air on the earth. The standard is discussed in PSIs, Pounds per Square Inch, which, at sea level, is about 15. In other words, the pressure on a square inch of surface at sea level is about 15 pounds.

mountain wave—A strong stable mass of air that flows over a mountain and meets a blanket of unstable air on the other side. Mechanically, the strong, stable air will rush up one side of the mountain and down the other. When it strikes the valley floor, it will rebound, where it will strike the bottom of the unstable air mass. Not being able to punch a hole through, it will rebound toward earth again. If the conditions are right, this bouncing effect can be felt hundreds of miles away from the mountain that caused the condition.

nimbus—The suffix that is added to the name of a cloud to indicate that it is a storm system. Cumulonimbus, for instance, means that the cumulus cloud is in fact a storm cloud. A nimbus cloud is usually dark and often anvil-shaped and, at a distance, rain can be seen as dark lines that extend from the nimbus cloud to the surface of the earth.

OBS—Omni-bearing selector. *See* course selector.

offshore breeze—*See* pressure system.

onshore breeze—*See* pressure system.

overloading—A very stupid and dangerous thing to do.

PanAm weather—An old bush pilot term meaning atmospheric conditions that were clear, clear, clear.

preflight—A step-by-step check of the plane to make certain that it is ready and adequate for flying safely.

pressure system—A system where moisture-laden, warm air rises until it cools. Then it falls to earth where it is re-warmed to rise again. The classical system has warm air rising over land and drifting over a body of water where it cools and falls. Then, because of the circular movement of the air mass, it blows onshore where it is once again heated and rises. At night, this process is reversed, since land loses heat faster than water, and there is an offshore breeze.

radials—Any one of the directional signals emitted by a VOR station.

relative humidity—The ability of the air to absorb water vapors. If the relative humidity is high, that means that the air is absorbing moisture. If the relative humidity is low, that means that the air cannot hold the vapors and they will fall out as precipitation: snow, rain, sleet and hail. *See* dew point.

runway and terrain slope illusion—A condition in which the pilot believes he is too high or too low on landing. In attempting to correct the descent, the pilot will overcompensate and place himself and his aircraft in danger.

runway width illusion—An illusion brought about by a narrow runway that causes a pilot to feel that he is too high on landing.

shear—*See* wind shear.

slant range—The distance in nautical miles from a plane and a VOR station as indicated by the DME. This is a line-of-sight distance and is affected by the altitude of the plane.

small lake takeoff—A circular maneuver on a small lake to build up enough speed to take off.

snap—A sudden change in the temperature. A cold snap is a sudden cooling wind that can drop the temperature scores of degrees overnight. A warm snap, also known as a chinook, can raise the temperature a score of degrees in the same time.

spatial orientation—An illusion in which objects that cannot move appear to do so.

station pressure—The atmospheric reading at a particular station. This is important to a pilot because an altimeter measures pressure, not altitude. As an example, at sea level, a plane at 3,000 feet will have an altimeter reading of 3,000 feet. If that same plane flies over a 1,000-foot mountain, the altimeter will still read 3,000 feet. If a pilot pre-sets an airport's pressure into his or her altimeter, the pilot will be able to use the altimeter to assist in landing.

STOL—Short takeoff and landing. Modifications made to an airplane such that it can take off and land on a shorter runway.

stratosphere—That portion of the atmosphere that is 40 to 60 miles off the surface of the earth.

stratus clouds—The clouds that form low decks or, to pilots, a ceiling.

sun dog—Pillar-like rainbows or complete rainbow halos around the sun caused by the reflection of the sun's rays on ice crystals or water droplets in the atmosphere.

swamper—In the early days of aviation, someone who traded his services for flying lessons.

tailwind—A wind that is pushing the plane toward its destination. *See* crosswind.

thermals—Updrafts of warm air, often laden with water vapors. The area where a thermal is present is known as a high pressure zone. *See* low pressure.

Three-Cell circulation—The three different global weather cells: from the equator or 30 degrees north and south; from 30 degrees north and south to 60 degrees north and south; and from 60 degrees to each pole. The term implies the ongoing weather systems that affect global weather conditions.

tiedowns—An anchor and rope or cable system to tie a plane in its storage area.

TO-FROM Indicator—The switch on the VOR receiver that indicates if you are locked onto a radial and going TO the VOR station or FROM the VOR station.

transponder—An instrument that is coupled with an encoding altimeter that transmits an identification code. Received by air traffic controllers, the plane's altitude, speed, and distance appear on the radar screen, which enables the controllers to know exactly where each plane is located.

troposphere—That portion of the atmosphere that is 45,000 to 65,000 feet above the surface of the earth.

tundra tires—Large tires specifically designed for landing on the tundra.

turbulence—Unstable air masses.

Vasalva Maneuver—Pinching your nose, closing your mouth, and very gently blowing. This will force pressure up the eustachian tube and allow your ears to "pop." This maneuver, however, is only good when you descend.

venturi effect—The effect of a wind blowing up a valley or canyon. Since the wind cannot "spread out," it rebounds off the valley walls and returns to the center of the canyon. This causes turbulence in the canyon.

vertical landing—A landing in which a strong wind is used to land the plane vertically.

VFR—Visual flight rules, meaning that you are flying on the basis of what you can see and not depending on instruments.

VOR—Very high frequency omnidirectional range. A VOR station will emit "radials" of electronic pulse, which a VOR indicator in an airplane will receive. By locking onto a radial, a pilot can navigate by an electronic beam.

VOR receiver—The equipment in the cockpit that receives the VOR radials and locks onto the directional beam.

warm front—A mass of warm air that usually means good weather.

warm snap—*See* chinook.

water vapor—The primary component of the weather. As the ability of the air to retain water vapor is reduced by temperature, the chances of precipitation in the form of rain, snow, sleet, or hail increase.

weather—The study of the changing conditions of the atmosphere and the prediction of the air's ability to move and/or retain moisture.

weather pattern—A fancy way of saying the state of the weather in terms of pressure systems, wind, clouds, and precipitation.

weather forecaster—A man or woman who will tell you tomorrow why what he or she predicted yesterday didn't happen today.

wet compass—A compass that sits on top of the instrument panel and is full of liquid. As the plane turns, the interior dial of the compass adjusts itself in sequence.

What If game—A mind game that a pilot plays by himself. For example, the pilot would be flying along at 3,000 feet and say to himself, "What if the right engine caught on fire?" Then, in his mind, he would go through the procedures to resolve that problem. Perhaps an hour later he would think of another problem and resolve that one as well. The point of the game is to prepare yourself for what to do if any of the "What If" scenarios ever came to pass.

whiteout—An atmospheric condition where the sky and earth blend so that there is no visible horizon.

williwaw—A sudden, violent storm unique to the Aleutian Islands.

wind—The movement of air masses.

wind shear—A sudden, violent cross wind that can momentarily move a plane out of its intended path of travel. This can be a deadly condition if it happens while a plane is landing.

wind sock—A bag on a pole that can swivel and gather wind. When inflated, it indicates in which direction the wind is blowing.

Bibliography

Anderson, Eric G. *Plane Safety and Survival*. Blue Ridge Summit, PA.: TAB/AERO. 1978.

Brown Jr., Thomas, and Brandt Morgan. *Tom Brown's Field Guide to City and Urban Survival*. New York: Berkeley Publishing Group. 1984.

Buck, Robert N. *Weather Flying*. New York: Macmillan. 1970.

Cohen, Stan. *Flying Beats Work*. Missoula, Mont.: Pictorial Histories Publishing Company. 1988.

Christy, Joe. *The Private Pilot's Handy Reference Manual*. Blue Ridge Summit, PA.: TAB Books. 1981.

——————. *Your Pilot's License*. Blue Ridge Summit, PA.: TAB Books.

——————. *Good Takeoffs and Good Landings—Second Edition*. Blue Ridge Summit, PA.: TAB Books. 1991.

Craighead Jr., Frank C. and John J. Craighead. *How to Survive On Land and Sea*. Annapolis, Md.: Naval Institute Press. 1984.

Day, Beth. *Glacier Pilot*. Fort Worth, Texas: Holt, Rinehart & Winston. 1957.

Dwyer, James E. *The Private Pilot's Bluebook*. Stein and Day. 1977.

Fear, Gene. *Surviving the Unexpected Wilderness Emergency*. Olympia, Wash.: Survival Education Association. 1972.

Fillingham, Paul. *Basic Guide to Flying*. Redding, Calif.: Hawthorn Books. 1975.

Geeting, Doug, and Steve Woerner. *Mountain Flying*. Blue Ridge Summit, PA.: TAB Books. 1988.

Greiner, James. *Wager with the Wind*. Chicago: Rand McNally & Co. 1974.

Griffin, Jeff W. *Cold Weather Flying*. Blue Ridge Summit, PA.: TAB Books. 1979.

Harkey, Ira B. *Pioneer Bush Pilot*. Seattle: University of Washington Press. 1974.

Helmericks, Harmon. *The Last of the Bush Pilots*. New York: Alfred A. Knopf. 1970.

Hoyt, John R. *Safety After Solo*. PAn American Navigation Series. 1966.

Janson, Lone E. *Mudhole Smith*. Bothell, Wash.: Alaska Northwest Books. 1981.

Kershner, William K. *The Advanced Pilot's Flight Manual*. Ames, Iowa: Iowa State University Press. 1970.

_____. *The Student Pilot's Flight Manual*. Ames, Iowa: Iowa State University Press. 1979.

Newton, Dennis. *Severe Weather Flying*. New York: McGraw-Hill. 1983.

Platten, David. *The Outdoors Survival Handbook*. North Pomfret, Vt.: David & Charles. 1979.

Potter, Jean. *Flying Frontiersman*. New York: Macmillan. 1956.

_____. *The Flying North*. New York: Bantam Books. 1945.

Robertson, Dougal. *Sea Survival*. New York: Praeger Publishers. 1975.

Sanders, Ti. *Weather: A User's Guide to the Atmosphere*. South Bend, Ind.: Icarus. 1985.

Tappan, Mel. *Tappan On Survival*. Rogue River, Ore.: Janus Press. 1981.

Taylor, Richard L. *Instrument Flying*. New York: Macmillan. 1986.

"The Epic of Flight." *The Bush Pilots*. Alexandria, Va.: Time/Life Books. 1983.

The United States Armed Forces Survival Manual. Phillips, Maine: Rawson, Wade Publishing. 1980.

Thompson, Phillip D., Robert O'Brien, and the editors of LIFE. *Weather*. New York: Time, Inc. 1956.

Wilson, Jack. *Glacier Wings and Tales*. Anchorage: Great Northwest Publishing. 1988.

Index